eturn

EDITED BY MIKE ROYSTON

A NEW WINDMILL BOOK OF

VERY SHORT STORIES

Heinemann
New Windmills

Heinemann Educational Publishers
Halley Court, Jordan Hill, Oxford OX2 8EJ
A division of Reed Educational and Professional Publishing Ltd

OXFORD MELBOURNE AUCKLAND
JOHANNESBURG BLANTYRE GABORONE
IBADAN PORTSMOUTH (NH) USA CHICAGO

06 05 04 03 02
10 9 8 7 6 5 4 3 2 1

ISBN 0 435 13058 7

Acknowledgements
The publishers gratefully acknowledge the following for permission to reproduce copyright material.
Every effort has been made to trace copyright holders, but in some cases this has proved impossible.
The publishers would be happy to hear from any copyright holder that has not been acknowledged.

August House Publishers, Inc. for 'There Ain't Been No News' by Richard and Judy Dockrey Young from
Ozark Tall Tales, collected and edited by Richard and Judy Dockrey Young. Copyright © Richard and
Judy Dockrey Young 1989; Penguin Books, Australia for 'Ex-Poser' by Paul Jennings from
Unmentionable, published by Penguin Books, Australia; David Higham Associates Ltd for an extract
from 'The One That Got Away' by Jan Mark from *Story Chest: 100 Bedtime Stories*, published by Viking
Kestrel; Faber and Faber Ltd for 'Feeding the Dog' by Susan Price from *Here Lies Prices*, published by
Faber and Faber Ltd; Atheneum Books for Young Readers, an imprint of Simon & Schuster Children's
Publishing Division for *The Dancing Skeleton* by Cynthia C. DeFelice. Text Copyright © Cynthia C.
DeFelice 1989; The O'Brien Press Ltd for 'No Exit' by Aoife Cahill from *The Whole Shebang: McDonald's
Young Writers 1998*, published by The O'Brien Press Ltd; Hugh Oliver for 'The Christmas Gift', found in
The Oxford Book of Christmas Stories edited by Dennis Pepper, published by Oxford University Press;
Oxford University Press for 'Spider's Web' by Kathleen Arnott from *Tales from Africa*, published by
Oxford University Press; Rosemary A. Thurber and The Barbara Hogenson Agency for 'The Shrike and
the Chipmunks' by James Thurber from *Fables for Our Time*. Copyright © James Thurber 1940.
Copyright © renewed by Helen Thurber and Rosemary A. Thurber 1968. All rights reserved; Dennis
Hamley for 'George Bunnage' previously entitled 'Crossings' from *The Shirt Off A Hanged Man's Back*,
published by Deutsch, 1984. Copyright © Dennis Hamley; Marilyn Watts for 'Digging for Trouble' from
The Oxford Book of Funny Stories, published by Oxford University Press, 1995. Copyright © Marilyn
Watts; Scott Meredith Literary Agency Inc. for 'Nightmare in Blue' by Frederic Brown; Paul Groves for
'Sting' by Paul Groves and Nigel Grimshaw from *13 Sci Fi Stories*, published by Edward Arnold, 1970s;
David Higham Associates Ltd for 'Breakfast' by James Herbert; A. M. Heath & Co. Ltd for 'The Hand that
Feeds Me' by Michael Z. Lewin. Copyright © Michael Z. Lewin; The Vines Agency Inc., New York for
'Dog, Cat and Baby' by Joe R. Lansdale from *Splinters: A Collection of Short Stories*, edited by R. Baines,
published by Oxford University Press Australia, 1998; The Women's Press Ltd for 'Well, Well, Well' by
Kate Hall from *A Girl's Best Friend*, edited by Christina Dunhill. First published in Great Britain by The
Women's Press Ltd, 1987, 34 Great Sutton Street, London EC1V 0LQ; David Higham Associates Ltd for
'Reunion' by Arthur C. Clarke from *The Wind From The Sun*, published by Gollancz; Curtis Brown Ltd,
New York for 'Starbride' by Anthony Boucher from *Thrilling Wonder Stories*, published in 1951; Oxford
University Press Australia 1998 for 'Sticks and Stones' by Anii Meithke from *Smithereens: A Collection of
Short* Stories, edited by R. Baines, published by Oxford University Press Australia, 1998; John Johnson
Ltd for 'The Bridge' by Jessie Kesson from *Where the Apple Ripens*, published by Chatto & Windus,
1985; C. O'Connell for 'Court Martial' from *The Oxford Book of Christmas Stories*, edited by Dennis
Pepper, published by Oxford University Press; Don Congdon Associates Inc. for 'The Aqueduct' by Ray
Bradbury. Copyright © Ray Bradbury 1980.

Cover design by The Point
Cover illustration by Ian Bosworth
Illustrations by Jon Holder: *There Ain't Been No News, The Dancing Skeleton,
The Christmas Gift, Sting, The Bridge*.
Illustrations by Hashim Akib: *The One That Got Away, Digging for Trouble,
The Hand That Feeds Me, Starbride, The Aqueduct*.
Typeset by ⚡ Tek-Art, Croydon, Surrey
Printed and bound in the United Kingdom by Clays Ltd, St Ives plc

Contents

Year 9 and above

Introduction for students

Most stories in this book last between five and ten minutes. Some are shorter still. But they are all *genuine* stories with a beginning, a middle and an end, about people and situations you will easily relate to.

You can use the book to dip into and find your own favourites. There are stories about school, family, friends, aliens, witches, ghosts, killer cats and giant mutant bees. There's also a wide range of different types of story: horror, mystery, romance, fantasy, science fiction, fable, etc. I've tried to include something for every taste, and to cater for both confident and less confident readers.

The stories can be used in your English lessons. The Activities at the back of the book will help improve your skills as a reader and a writer. They are planned to fit the National Literacy Strategy for Key Stage 3. Mainly, though, they are there to increase your enjoyment of what you read and your understanding of how very short stories work.

Some of these stories are by people of your age. You don't need to be a professional author to get your work published. Start on your own PC, or by printing a class story collection . . . or by sending them to me, c/o Heinemann Educational Books at the address at the top of page ii. Perhaps your name will be on the Contents page of *A New Windmill Book of Very Short Stories, Volume 2*.

Mike Royston

Introduction for teachers

Why 'very short' stories?
Very short stories work in the classroom. The best ones offer teachers an invaluable resource because they:

- arrest attention and engage imagination without preliminaries
- are accessible, providing students with a brief, focused reading experience which (unlike an extract) satisfies their need for whole-text narrative
- provoke personal response: teachers know how to exploit 'That's weird!' as well as how to capitalize on 'That's brilliant!' for the purposes they have in mind
- lend themselves well to reading aloud by the teacher and by students, without being daunting to either
- provide a wide range of writing models: very short stories tend to be innovative in style and structure, encouraging students to try out new narrative forms which are within their scope
- are versatile: they can be used equally well to teach the NLS, to begin/extend/round off a Scheme of Work, or to be enjoyed for their own sake.

The structure of the collection
The 25 stories in this collection are targeted at the whole of Key Stage 3. Broadly speaking, they progress through the volume in terms of reading difficulty and appropriateness of subject matter for Years 7, 8 and 9. They are drawn from a range of cultural contexts.

With three exceptions (*There Ain't Been No News*, *Crossing* and *Well, Well, Well*), the stories are paired according to theme and/or genre. The pairings facilitate comparison, a vital reading skill, and offer teachers material to incorporate into existing or future Schemes of Work.

The Activities

The Activities at the end of the book are explicitly based on objectives in the Framework for Teaching English for Key Stage 3. They address Speaking & Listening and Writing Objectives as well as those specified for Reading.

The chart on pages 111 to 113, though far from exhaustive, directs teachers to the main Framework Objectives covered in each set of Activities for work at Sentence Level (S), Text Level – Reading (R), Text Level – Writing (W), and in Speaking & Listening (S&L). The coding used there is that of the DfEE *Framework for Teaching English: Years 7, 8 and 9*, issued April 2001.

Mike Royston

There Ain't Been No News
Richard and Judy Dockrey Young

Once there was a man down in Fort Smith, Arkansas, that ran a 'feed, seed and everything you need' store, but in order to do his business he travelled a lot by train. When he'd go away he'd get his cousin Fred to look after the farm chores for him. Well, he was gone for weeks one time, and came home, and he'd wired Fred to meet him at the station.

'Fred,' he said when he saw him, 'what's the news?'

'Oh, Henry,' said Fred, 'there ain't been no news.'

'You mean to say there ain't been no news, and me gone for weeks?'

'Nope,' said Fred. 'There ain't been no news. Oh . . . except your dog died. But other than that, there ain't been no news.'

'My dog died?' said Henry. 'What happened to him?'

'Well, that's easy to explain,' said Fred. 'He ate too much burned horse meat. But other than that, there ain't been no news.'

'Wait a minute,' said Henry. 'Where'd my dog get ahold of burned horse meat?'

'Well, that's easy to explain,' said Fred. 'When your barn burned to the ground it killed all your livestock, and your dog got ahold of too much burned horse meat, and died. But other than that, there ain't been no news.'

'My barn burned?' said Henry. 'What caused my barn to burn?'

'Well,' said Fred, 'that's easy to explain. It was sparks. Sparks from the house set the barn ablaze, and killed all your livestock, and your dog got ahold of too much burned horse meat, and ate it, and died. But other than that, there ain't been no news.'

'Sparks from the house?' said Henry. 'What happened to my house? Did my house burn down?' Fred was nodding solemn-like. 'What burned my house down?'

'Oh, Henry, that's easy to explain,' said Fred. 'It was the candles, they set the curtains on fire. All them candles around the coffin. They set the curtains on fire and burned the house down, and sparks from the house set the barn ablaze, and the barn burned down and killed all your livestock, and your dog got ahold of too much burned horse meat, and died. But other than that, there ain't been no news.'

'*What coffin?*' hollered Henry, lifting Fred off the landing by his lapels. '*Who died?*'

'Now, Henry,' said Fred, 'that's easy to explain. Your mother-in-law died, and we had the **wake** in the parlour, and the candles set the curtains on fire and burned the house down, and the sparks from the house set the barn

---

wake: a gathering of family and friends after a funeral

ablaze, and burned the barn down, and killed all your livestock, and your dog got ahold of too much burned horse meat, and ate it, and died. But other than that, there ain't been no news.'

'WHAT HAPPENED TO MY MOTHER-IN-LAW?' yelled Henry, shaking Fred around in the air.

'Oh . . . Henry . . . we've been arguing about that. Some says one thing and some says another. But as near as we can figure, she died of a broken heart when your wife ran off with the seed clerk.

'But other than that, there ain't been a bit of news!'

Ex Poser
Paul Jennings

There are two rich kids in our form. Sandra Morris and Ben Fox. They are both snobs. They think they are too good for the rest of us. Their parents have big cars and big houses. Both of them are quiet. They keep to themselves. I guess they don't want to mix with the ruffians like me.

Ben Fox always wears expensive gym shoes and the latest fashions. He thinks he is good-looking with his blue eyes and blond hair. He is a real poser.

Sandra Morris is the same. And she knows it. Blue eyes and blonde hair too. Skin like silk. Why do some kids get the best of everything?

Me, I landed pimples. I've used everything I can on them. But still they bud and grow and burst. Just when you don't want them to. It's not fair.

Anyway, today I have the chance to even things up. Boffin is bringing along his latest invention – a lie detector. Sandra Morris is the victim. She agreed to try it out because everyone knows that she would never tell a lie. What she doesn't know is that Boffin and I are going to ask her some very embarrassing questions.

Boffin is a brain. His inventions always work. He is smarter than the teachers. Everyone knows that. And now he has brought along his latest effort. A lie detector.

He tapes two wires to Sandra's arm. 'It doesn't hurt,' he says. 'But it is deadly accurate.' He switches on the machine and a little needle swings into the middle of the dial. 'Here's a trial question,' he says. 'Are you a girl?'

Sandra nods.

'You have to say yes or no,' he says.

'Yes,' replies Sandra. The needle swings over to TRUTH. Maybe this thing really works. Boffin gives a big grin.

'This time tell a lie,' says Boffin. 'Are you a girl?' he asks again.

Sandra smiles with that lovely smile of hers. 'No,' she says. A little laugh goes up but then all the kids in the room gasp. The needle points to LIE. This lie detector is a terrific invention.

'Okay,' says Boffin. 'You only have seven questions, David. The batteries will go flat after another seven questions.' He sits down behind his machine and twiddles the knobs.

This is going to be fun. I am going to find out a little bit about Sandra Morris and Ben Fox. It's going to be very interesting. Very interesting indeed.

I ask my first question. 'Have you ever kissed Ben Fox?'

Sandra goes red. Ben Fox goes red. I have got them this time. I am sure they have something going between them. I will expose them.

'No,' says Sandra. Everyone cranes their neck to see what the lie detector says. The needle points to TRUTH.

This is not what I expected. And I only have six questions left. I can't let her off the hook. I am going to expose them both.

'Have you ever held his hand?'

Again she says, 'No.' And the needle says TRUTH. I am starting to feel guilty. Why am I doing this?

I try another tack. 'Are you in love?' I ask.

A red flush starts to crawl up her neck. I am feeling really mean now. Fox is blushing like a sunset.

'Yes,' she says. The needle points to TRUTH.

I shouldn't have let the kids talk me into doing this. I decide to put Sandra and Ben out of their agony. I won't actually name him. I'll spare her that. 'Is he in this room?' I say.

She looks at the red Ben Fox. 'Yes,' she says. The needle points to TRUTH.

'Does he have blue eyes?' I ask.

'No,' she says.

'Brown?' I say.

'No,' she says again.

I don't know what to say next. I look at each kid in class very carefully. Ben Fox has blue eyes. I was sure that she loved him.

'This thing doesn't work,' I say to Boffin. 'I can't see one kid who doesn't have either blue eyes or brown eyes.'

'We can,' says Boffin. They are all looking at me.

I can feel *my* face turning red now. I wish I could sink through the floor but I get on with my last question. 'Is he an idiot?' I ask.

Sandra is very embarrassed. 'Yes,' she says in a voice that is softer than a whisper. 'And he has green eyes.'

The One That Got Away
Jan Mark

'And what have we to remember to bring tomorrow?'
Mrs Cooper asked, at half past three. Malcolm, sitting
near the back, wondered why she said 'we'. *She* wasn't
going to bring anything.

'Something interesting, Mrs Cooper,' said everyone
else, all together.

'And what are we going to do then?'

'Stand up and talk about it, Mrs Cooper.'

'So don't forget. All right. Chairs on tables. Goodbye,
Class Four.'

'Goodbye, Mrs Cooper. Goodbye, everybody.'

It all came out ever so slow, like saying prayers in
assembly. 'Amen,' said Malcolm, very quietly. Class Four
put its chairs on the tables, collected its coats and went
home, talking about all the interesting things it would
bring into school tomorrow.

Malcolm walked by himself. Mrs Cooper had first told
them to find something interesting on Monday. Now it was
Thursday and still he had not come up with any bright
ideas. There were plenty of things that he found
interesting, but the trouble was, they never seemed to
interest anyone else. Last time this had happened he had
brought along his favourite stone and shown it to the class.

'Very nice, Malcolm,' Mrs Cooper had said. 'Now tell us
what's interesting about it.' He hadn't known what to say.
Surely anyone looking at the stone could see how
interesting it was.

Mary was going to bring her gerbil. James, Sarah, and
William had loudly discussed rare shells and fossils, and
the only spider in the world with five legs.

'It can't be a spider then,' said David, who was
eavesdropping.

'It had an accident,' William said.

Isobel intended to bring her pocket calculator and
show them how it could write her name by punching in
738051 and turning it upside down. She did this every
time, but it still looked interesting.

Malcolm could think of nothing.

When he reached home he went up to his bedroom
and looked at the shelf where he kept important things;
his twig that looked like a stick insect, his marble that
looked like a glass eye, the penny with a hole in it and the
Siamese-twin jelly-babies, one red, one green and stuck
together, back to back. He noticed that they were now
stuck to the shelf, too. His stone had once been there as
well, but after Class Four had said it was boring he had
put it back in the garden. He still went to see it
sometimes.

What he really needed was something that could move
about, like Mary's gerbil or William's five-legged spider.
He sat down on his bed and began to think.

On Friday, after assembly, Class Four began to be
interesting. Mary kicked off with the gerbil that whirred
round its cage like a hairy balloon with the air escaping.
Then they saw William's lame spider, James's fossil,
Jason's collection of snail shells stuck one on top of the
other like the leaning tower of Pisa, and David's bottled
conkers that he had kept in an air-tight jar for three years.
They were still as glossy as new shoes.

Then it was Malcolm's turn. He went up to the front
and held out a matchbox. He had chosen it very carefully.
It was the kind with the same label top and bottom so
that when you opened it you could never be sure that it
was the right way up and all the matches fell out. Malcolm

---

eavesdropping: listening in the background

opened it upside down and jumped. Mrs Cooper jumped too. Malcolm threw himself down on hands and knees and looked under her desk.

'What's the matter?' Mrs Cooper said.

'It's fallen out!' Malcolm cried.

'What is it?' Mrs Cooper said, edging away.

'I don't know – it's got six legs and sharp knees . . . and sort of frilly ginger eyebrows on stalks—.' He pounced. 'There it goes.'

'Where?'

'Missed it,' said Malcolm. 'It's running under your chair, Mary.'

Mary squeaked and climbed onto the table because she thought that was the right way to behave when creepy-crawlies were about.

'I see it!' Jason yelled, and jumped up and down. David threw a book in the direction that Jason was pointing and James began beating the floor with a rolled-up comic.

'I got it – I killed it,' he shouted.

'It's crawling up the curtains,' Sarah said and Mrs Cooper, who was standing by the curtains, moved rapidly away from them.

'It's over by the door,' Mary shrieked, and several people ran to head it off. Chairs were overturned.

Malcolm stood by Mrs Cooper's desk with his matchbox. His contribution was definitely the most interesting thing that anyone had seen that morning. He was only sorry that he hadn't seen it himself.

Feeding The Dog
Susan Price

This story's supposed to be true.

It's about a witch, one of the really bad kind, a man named Downing.

He'd spent years learning witchcraft, travelling all over the country, to meet other witches and be taught by them. He married a witch's daughter, and they had a horde of children. They kept a pack of cats too, who went out to steal for them, bringing back meat and fish from other people's tables. There were just as many children as there were cats, and some people said the children *were* the cats; and the only people who doubted this were the people who thought that the children were worse than the cats. Downing and his wife cared just as much for all of them, and anybody who raised hand or stone against either children or cats had to spend the next few days in bed, aching all over, cursed by Witch Downing. And everybody knew that Witch Downing could do worse than make you ache. So, mostly, the little Downings, human and **feline**, got away with their thieving.

But a farmer named Hollis heard noises in his yard one night, and came out to find three of Downing's children tormenting the pigs in his sty, by hitting them with sticks. He shouted at them and told them to go away, and they threw stones at him, and shouted names. Hollis was so angry then that he forgot about Witch Downing. The children were so used to getting away with everything that they didn't try to run away. Hollis laid hold of the

feline: cat

eldest and gave him the first **hiding** he'd ever had in his life. The other two ran away when they saw what was happening to their brother. They ran home and told their father.

Witch Downing went to see Farmer Hollis the next day, and demanded money in compensation for the terrible injuries inflicted on his poor boy. Farmer Hollis was afraid of what he had done, but he wouldn't back down now, and he said, 'What terrible injuries? I've done him no more harm than I've done my own sons – I've only given him the sore backside that he should have had a long time ago from you if you'd been any kind of a father! What favour do you think you're doing him, letting him grow up thinking he can do whatever he pleases?'

'Don't preach at me!' Witch Downing said. He went home, thinking that no curse he'd ever set on anybody before was bad enough for Hollis.

So he made a thing. He killed a couple of his cats, and he caught a big dog, and he killed that too. He used poisons, and some of the worst magic he'd learned, and he made this thing that he called a dog – it looked something like a dog. But it was so black that you couldn't really see it, and its eyes shone all the time like a real dog's eyes do when light catches them – shone red, or green, and sometimes blue. It was big. At midnight Downing said to it, 'Hollis.' The thing went out, and it didn't come back that night. The next day Farmer Hollis was missing from his bed, and couldn't be found anywhere.

Witch Downing boasted that he knew what had happened to Hollis, and that people had better watch out! No one knew what he meant.

That night, Downing woke up and saw two bright green candleflames floating beside his bed. There was a

---

hiding: a hard smacking

shape around them, a blackness. Then the candleflames burned red, and teeth showed beneath them. It was the thing, the dog, come back. It sat beside Witch Downing's bed and looked at him. When he asked what it wanted, it made no movement or sound, but waited. When Downing tried to leave his bed, it growled, and he lay back quickly. He spoke **incantations** for dismissing spirits, but it stayed. At last he said, 'Farmer Hollis's wife.' Then the thing rose and went out.

People began to disappear. Farmer Hollis had vanished, and then his wife had disappeared the night after. The following day the Vicar couldn't be found; and then a market woman vanished. On the fifth night, the disappearance was of a woman who'd chased the witch's cats away with pepper, and on the sixth night, Farmer Hollis's little son.

But Downing no longer boasted. Now he slunk about and jumped if a dog barked.

People who had nothing much to stay for began to leave the town, and Downing began to run out of names. Night after night the thing came, sat beside his bed, and waited. It was very patient. It waited and waited as Downing, all in a sweat, tried to think of a name he hadn't given it before. Sometimes he kept it waiting almost until morning, and the closer morning came, the more excited the thing was. It panted like a real dog, and stirred where it sat. Downing didn't want to find out what would happen if he kept the thing until morning, and he would gabble out, 'The boy who serves at the greengrocer's!' or 'The girl in the green skirt that I pass in the lane!' And the thing would rise and go out.

Then came a night when Downing, worn out as he was, must have dozed. He woke with a great shock, and saw that the sky was turning pink! And the thing was pacing

---

incantations: charms

up and down by his bed, whining with excitement. 'My wife!' Downing cried – and the thing leapt over him and onto his wife. There was a dreadful noise. Downing jumped from the bed and ran away. There was not an eyelash left of his wife when he returned.

But the thing came to his bedside that night; and he could think of no one. When the thing began to wave its tail, he said, 'The baby.' And there was no baby in its cot when Downing got up.

'My eldest son,' he said, the next night; and on nights after that, 'My eldest daughter – Billy – Anne – Mary . . .' And when the last of his children had gone, the thing still came, sat beside him, fixed its eyes on him, and waited.

Downing had nothing to say. Towards dawn, the silence was filled with the drumming of the thing's tail on the floorboards, and a whine from its throat. The light increased – the thing couldn't stay any longer, and its master hadn't fed it. So it ate its master before it left – and who knows where it went, or where it is now?

For all Downing's learning, he had never learned that you can't dine with the Devil without becoming the meal.

The Dancing Skeleton
Cynthia C. DeFelice

Aaron Kelly was dead.

There wasn't anything anybody could do about it. And, to tell you the truth, nobody much cared. Aaron had been so downright mean and **ornery** in his life that folks were glad to see him go. Even his widow never shed a tear. She just bought a coffin, put Aaron in it, and buried him. Goodbye, Aaron Kelly, and good riddance!

But that very night, Aaron got up out of his grave, walked through the graveyard, and came home. His widow was sitting in the parlour, thinking how peaceful and quiet it was without Aaron around, when he walked right in the door.

'What's all this?' he shouted. 'You're all dressed in black. You look like someone died. Who's dead?'

The widow pointed a shaking finger at Aaron.

'You are!' she said.

'Oh, no, I ain't!' hollered Aaron. 'I don't feel dead. I feel fine!'

'Well you don't look fine,' said the widow. 'You look dead! Now you just get yourself back in that coffin where you belong.'

'Oh, no,' said Aaron. 'I ain't goin' back to that coffin till I feel dead.'

Just plain ornery, he was.

Well, since Aaron wouldn't go back to the grave, his widow couldn't collect the life insurance. Without that money, she couldn't pay for the coffin. If she didn't pay for the coffin, the undertaker might take it back. And if he

ornery: disagreeable

did that, she'd *never* be rid of Aaron! Aaron didn't care. He just sat in his favourite rocking-chair, rocking back and forth, back and forth, day after day, night after night. But after a while, Aaron began to dry up. Pretty soon he was nothing but a skeleton.

Every time he rocked, his old bones clicked and clacked. His widow did her best to ignore him, but it wasn't easy with all the racket he made.

Then one night, the best fiddler in town came to call on Aaron's widow. He'd heard Aaron was dead, and he thought he might marry the woman himself.

The fiddler and the widow sat down together, cosylike, on the bench . . . and ole Aaron sat right across from them, just a-creakin' and a-crackin' and a-grinnin'. Fiddler said, 'Woman, how long am I going to have to put up with that old bag o'bones sitting there? I can't court you proper with him staring at me like that!' Widow answered, 'I know! But what can we do?'

The fiddler shrugged. The widow sighed. The clock ticked. And Aaron rocked. Finally, Aaron said, 'Well, *this* ain't any fun at all. Fiddler, take out your fiddle. I feel like dancin'!'

So the fiddler took out his fiddle and began to play. My, my! He could make that fiddle sing!

Aaron Kelly heard that sweet music and he couldn't sit still. He stood up. Oooh, his dry bones felt stiff! He shook himself. He cracked his knucklebones – aah! And he began to dance.

With his toe bones a-tappin' and his feet bones a-flappin', round and round he danced like a fool! With his finger bones a-snappin' and his arm bones a-clappin', how that dead man did dance!

The music grew wilder, and so did Aaron until, suddenly, a bone broke loose from that dancing skeleton, flew through the air, and landed on the floor with a CLATTER!

'Oh, my!' cried the fiddler. 'Look at that! He's dancing so hard, he's *falling apart*!'

'Well, then,' said the widow, '*play faster!*'

The fiddler played faster.

Bones began flying every which way, and still that skeleton danced!

'*Play louder!*' cried the widow.

The fiddler hung on to that fiddle. He fiddled a tune that made the popcorn pop. He fiddled a tune that made the bedbugs hop. He fiddled a tune that made the rocks get up and dance! Crickety-crack, down and back!

Old Aaron went a-hoppin', his dry bones a-poppin'. Flippin' and floppin', they just kept droppin'!

Soon there was nothing left of Aaron but a pile of bones lying still on the floor . . . all except for the old bald head bone, and *that* looked up at the fiddler, snapped its yellow teeth, and said,

'O O O O O W E E E ! AIN'T WE HAVING FUN!'

It was all too much for the fiddler. He dropped his fiddle, said, 'Woman, I'm getting out of here!' and ran out the door. The widow gathered up Aaron's bones and carried them back to the graveyard. She put them in the coffin and mixed them all around in there, so Aaron could never put himself back together.

After that, Aaron Kelly stayed in his grave where he belonged.

But folks say that if you walk by the graveyard on a still summer night when the crickets are fiddling their tunes, you'll hear a faint clicking and clacking down under the ground.

And you'll know . . . it's Aaron's bones, still trying to dance.

And what about the fiddler and the widow?

Well, they never did get together again. Aaron Kelly had made DEAD SURE of that!

No Exit
Aoife Cahill

Here I am in my own personal prison, chained to the wall. My prison has no door and no window, just four walls. It's almost as if it was built for me. Maybe it was. Since I opened my eyes and had the strength to move I've been testing the walls for weaknesses, kicking and pummelling them as hard as I can.

Even though there are no doors, hatches or windows to put food through, I never feel hungry. There must be something wrong with my memory because I cannot remember anything before waking. Since then my eyes have adjusted to the dark and I can see quite well. I notice that even though I wear no clothes, I feel no cold. My prison is like a hot-water bottle, always warm.

I think that my captors like to torment me, as I can hear muffled voices outside of my prison. Sometimes they laugh and sometimes it is as if they are talking to me. The walls of my prison seem to be closing in on me.

I am beginning to grow lonely. I have no one to talk to or to interact with. The muffled voices are becoming clearer and I can understand some words. I call to the outsiders but they do not answer. I am desperate to be released. There seems to be no exit!

The walls have stopped closing in on me and I find it easier to move around. My chain is lighter now that I'm used to it. I'm growing frustrated and I flail at the walls in vain. 'I want out!' I scream. My tormentors tease me with silence.

I hear a noise. It sounds like a drum. Lub-Dum, Lub-Dum, Lub-Dum. It beats constantly. This sound moves around. It's very near now but I cannot pinpoint it exactly.

Something brushed up against me. There is someone else here! Now that we have met I do not feel lonely any more. Although we don't speak the same language we communicate using gestures. Sometimes both of us pound the walls until we exhaust ourselves.

Tonight I was awoken rudely. My friend was already awake. Suddenly a door opened and gloved hands pulled my friend from our prison. I heard cries of pain and anger from outside. The hands came for me. I was pulled roughly into the outside world. The pain was excruciating. I was held upside down and thumped on the back. I screamed. Somebody wrapped me in blankets. I was placed on a bed between my sister and my mother. I had been born.

The Christmas Gift
Hugh Oliver

It was Christmas Eve. All day it had been snowing – thick flakes that piled against the doors and covered the fields with a carpet of white. And in one of the lonely farmhouses on the Canadian prairie, a child was being born.

The child's father, John, paced the floor of the living-room. He was anxious. It was now three hours since his wife Jessie had begun to give birth. This was to be their first child. They were both old, and they had wanted a child for a long time.

'I wish that the doctor had been able to come,' thought John. 'If only the snow hadn't been so deep. But what am I worrying about? It happens to thousands every day. And Jessie's mother is up there with her.'

Outside in the darkness, everything was silent except for the gentle pattering of the snow flakes on the window and the trees creaking beneath their icy loads. As John sat in front of the wood fire, he heard a knock at the door. Imagining it might perhaps be the doctor, he was surprised, almost fearful, to find on the step a man he had never seen before.

'Will you give me shelter?' asked the stranger.

John hesitated. But seeing the stranger's sad appearance – snow blanketing his coat and even clinging to his hair – he invited him in. He helped him off with his coat, and said that he could spend the rest of the night in front of the fire. He gave the stranger food to eat, and the man was grateful.

'Why are you out on a snowy night like this?' asked John.

'I have much to do,' said the stranger. 'And I have far to go.'

'But where are you going?' asked John.

'In this world,' said the stranger, 'I go wherever they will welcome me.'

John thought him odd, but questioned him no more. The stranger warmed himself in silence for a while in front of the fire. Then John told him that his wife Jessie was at that moment giving birth to their first child in the room above.

'I know,' said the stranger.

'How can you know?' asked John.

'I heard her cry out,' he said.

But John had heard no sound.

The child was born at two o'clock in the morning. It was born dead. Jessie fell into an exhausted sleep. Her mother put the dead child into the cradle beside her. Then she went downstairs to tell John what had happened.

John was numb with despair. When he looked at the table spread with all the good things for Christmas, there was no joy in him any more.

'What was it?' he asked.

'A boy,' said Jessie's mother. 'Would you like to see him?'

'I would,' answered John. 'Then I'll take him away. I shouldn't like Jessie to see him – not dead.'

John went upstairs and looked lovingly at his sleeping wife. He was thankful that she had not been taken from him as well.

He gazed at the pathetic little body in the cradle. Then he lifted it out and carried it downstairs.

He stood holding the child, and his silence was his sorrow. The stranger asked if he might take the child. Saying nothing, John gave it to him. The stranger rocked the child in his arms and kissed the child's forehead.

'Why do you do that?' asked Jessie's mother. 'The child is dead.'

'He needs to be made warm,' said the stranger.

'But he's dead,' repeated Jessie's mother.

The stranger smiled and continued to rock the child.

And John watching saw the child's eyes open, and Jessie's mother listening heard the child cry out.

'Why, you have done a miracle,' shouted John. 'You have brought the child back from death.'

'He was not dead,' said the stranger. 'He had never lived.'

He gave the child to Jessie's mother. 'Quickly!' he said. 'Take him upstairs to his mother before she wakes.' He turned to John. 'And now,' he said, 'I must be on my way.'

John did not know what to do – to laugh for joy or to weep for joy, to kiss the stranger or what to do. 'You must stay,' he said. 'You must stay with us forever.' But the stranger stood at the door putting on his coat.

'At least stay for Christmas,' pleaded John. 'Look, I have all these good things.' He pointed to the table. 'And you who have made our happiness should share it.'

But the stranger would not stay. Thanking John for his kindness, he opened the door and walked out across the snow.

It had stopped snowing. John stood at the door, watching the stranger until he was out of sight. Then, as he turned to go indoors, he was filled with wonder; for he saw that where the stranger had walked, there were no footprints in the snow.

Spider's Web
Kathleen Arnott

The animals were lonely. They stood in the forest talking to one another, wondering how they could each get a wife to keep them company and to cook their food for them.

When Hare joined the group, he was soon able to tell them what to do.

'I have heard that there are plenty of wives up in the sky, beyond the clouds,' he said.

'But how shall we get there?' they asked.

'I will spin a strong web and fasten it on to a cloud,' said Spider, 'and then you will be able to climb up it, and find wives.'

So Spider began to spin, and very soon he was lost to sight high above them all with only the ladder of silver thread to show them the way he had gone. Presently Hare declared that all was ready and, leading the way, he began to climb up into the sky followed by all the other animals.

How the silken thread trembled as the elephant, the buffalo, the lion, and the monkey climbed higher and higher, while Hare turned back from time to time, urging them onwards.

At last they reached the country above the clouds and began to bargain for wives with the people there. Hare had been quite right when he said there were plenty of wives to be had, and soon most of the animals had chosen a wife and paid the agreed **dowry**.

Not so Hare. He chose his wife and made some excuse to her mother so that he did not pay the price

---

dowry: a gift made by a husband to his wife or her parents

immediately. Then he crept round the back of his future mother-in-law's hut, to see what he could find to eat. There was a large pile of **beniseed**, and Hare made a most satisfying meal of it while everyone else was busy talking about their new wives. Even Hare was surprised a little later, to see how small the beniseed heap had become, and felt somewhat **apprehensive** as to what the owner would say when she found out.

Of course, he soon thought of a way to get himself out of trouble, and taking a handful of beniseed he ambled across to where the animals were still busy talking and rubbed some seeds on to Spider, pretending to brush off some dust.

He was only just in time as the next moment a woman came stamping up to the group of animals, shouting angrily:

'Who has been stealing my beniseed? It's always the same. When you folk come up from the Earth something always gets stolen. Now, who did it this time?'

Of course, all the animals protested and said they were innocent, which indeed they were. Then the cunning Hare stood up and went towards his mother-in-law, putting on a kind, patient voice and saying:

'There is only one way of finding out who stole your beniseed. Let us search every animal and look for signs of seeds or leaves which are bound to have clung to the fur of the thief.'

The woman agreed and together she and Hare began to search the animals, none of whom objected since they knew they had stolen nothing.

Suddenly Hare gave a cry.

'Oh no!' he exclaimed. 'Not you, Spider! How could you have done such a thing?'

---

beniseed: a herb with white and mauve flowers
apprehensive: worried

'What are you talking about?' asked Spider, as the other animals crowded round him, and the woman seized him to have a closer look.

'Yes,' she said angrily. 'You have some beniseed clinging to your body. You must be the thief! Don't try to deny it.'

The other animals were angry too, telling Spider what a stupid thing he had done to steal from Hare's mother-in-law, and they would not listen when he swore he had done no such thing.

At last he managed to get away from them all, and calling out in disgust: 'I got you up here, but you can get yourselves down again,' he began his descent to Earth, rolling up his web as he went.

Now the animals were in a fix, for their ladder had gone, and it was a very long way down to Earth. They shouted to Spider and begged him to come back and spin another web for them, but he would not answer and at last they lost sight of him among the far-distant trees of the Earth.

'Now what shall we do?' they asked one another, for they had no desire to stay in the clouds for the rest of their lives.

'I'm going to jump,' said the monkey, suiting the action to the words, and with a mighty leap he dropped like a stone towards the Earth.

'So am I,' exclaimed the antelope, and he gave a bound after the monkey, and was followed by a number of other animals, all encouraged by Hare.

'That's right! That's splendid!' he kept saying, as animal after animal jumped from the clouds. But he did not tell them that they were jumping to their deaths, and as each one hit the ground he was killed outright.

All except Hare, of course. He stood back and waited beside the elephant, telling that large and cumbersome creature to wait until last in case he fell on one of his smaller brothers. Eventually, when all the animals had gone, Hare told the elephant it was safe for him to jump too.

'I'll come with you,' said Hare, leaping on to the elephant's head and clinging tightly as they sped through the air. The poor elephant landed with such a crash that he was killed at once, but his huge body saved Hare from striking the ground and he was not injured at all.

So the cunning animal ran off into the bush to look for Spider and to try to make friends with him again, simply because he hoped for Spider's help at some other time.

But since that day nobody has ever been able to climb up into the sky, and those who have heard this story have no wish to try.

The Shrike and the Chipmunks

James Thurber

Once upon a time there were two chipmunks, a male and a female. The male chipmunk thought that arranging nuts in artistic patterns was more fun than just piling them up to see how many you could pile up. The female was all for piling up as many as you could. She told her husband that if he gave up making designs with the nuts there would be room in their large cave for a great many more and he would soon become the wealthiest chipmunk in the woods. But he would not let her interfere with his designs, so she flew into a rage and left him.

'The **shrike** will get you,' she said, 'because you are helpless and cannot look after yourself.' To be sure, the female chipmunk had not been gone three nights before the male had to dress for a banquet and could not find his studs or shirt or suspenders. So he couldn't go to the banquet, but that was just as well because all the chipmunks who did go were attacked and killed by a weasel.

The next day the shrike began hanging around outside the chipmunk's cave, waiting to catch him. The shrike couldn't get in because the doorway was clogged up with soiled laundry and dirty dishes. 'He will come out for a walk after breakfast and I will get him then,' thought the shrike. But the chipmunk slept all day and did not get up and have breakfast until after dark. Then he came out for a breath of air before beginning work on a new design. The shrike swooped down to snatch the chipmunk, but could not see very well on account of the dark, so he

---

shrike: vicious bird of prey

batted his head against an alder branch and was killed.

A few days later the female chipmunk returned and saw the awful mess the house was in. She went to the bed and shook her husband. 'What would you do without me?' she demanded. 'Just go on living, I guess,' he said. 'You wouldn't last five days,' she told him. She swept the house and did the dishes and sent out the laundry, and then she made the chipmunk get up and wash and dress. 'You can't be healthy if you lie in bed all day and never get any exercise,' she told him. So she took him for a walk in the bright sunshine and they were both caught and killed by the shrike's brother, a shrike named Stoop.

MORAL: Early to rise and early to bed makes a man healthy and wealthy and dead.

Crossing
Dennis Hamley

George Bunnage leant forward into the wind. His right hand eased the throttle backward and the Suzuki burst forward at 75 miles an hour. The dawn autumnal mist seemed to part before the straight beam of his headlight. Deep-cut tyres bit into the wet road. Inside his leathers George was warm and secure: outside, a cold nip in the rushing air worried at the visor of his helmet and sent a chill round his forehead.

Only four miles to go.

His mind cast back to the last time he had travelled this road. Exactly a year ago. The same time: the same speed. The same houses, shops, trees; the same turnings, junctions; the same traffic lights. Even, it seemed, the same traffic coming the other way. But surely not the same ending to the journey? Why was he **traversing** this road again? As the Suzuki urged itself forward, George racked his brains but found no answer.

He remembered it all. A party till the small hours: then a breakneck ride home. Forty miles to go. In half an hour at that time of night? No trouble. Roaring, bucketing along, master of the smooth motor underneath him. King of the road, he had **exulted** to himself. I'm king of the road.

But was he now? Though he continued to rack his brains, he just did not know any more. His tight-fitting riding leathers seemed to grip tighter round his waist as he leant into a right-hand bend.

Yes, that night a year ago had been one to remember.

traversing: travelling
exulted: said triumphantly

If only he could remember it: if only the question that over-rode everything else would not keep surging into his mind. Well, that was partly why he was travelling this road again. But what good could he do?

George braked as he approached a turning to the left: as the Suzuki slowed, suddenly the grip round his waist tightened and he seemed to be pulled ever so slightly backwards.

Two miles to go. The mists were rising: the day would be fine. A year ago, they were closing in for a dull, dark day. Perhaps that was why it happened. George's mind was so confused that he could not tell any more. There seemed to be some sort of weight on his left shoulder; the grip round his waist was even tighter. He felt very conscious of his own body. The thought crossed his mind that he might be sickening for something.

A mile. Half a mile. A car parked by the road just ahead. Pull out to pass it. Look in the mirror first.

George caught his breath. In the mirror: what was it? A view back up the deserted road – yes. But what else? What was behind him? What shadow seemed to be over his shoulder? A trick of light as the sun began to rise?

It must be. The whole affair was ludicrous. Nothing had happened last year in the next quarter of a mile. It had all been his imagination, and the urge to retrace his steps a year later was absolute lunacy.

Very close now. Soon he would see the lights of that pedestrian crossing, deserted at night but still sending out its meaningless message with no one to heed it – red, green, flashing amber. No one to heed it in the early morning – so who cares if the light is red? Straight through it: don't slacken speed.

All right on a bright morning like this. Nearly all right on a dark, dark dawn with the fog coming. Chances are always worth taking when you think you can get away with them.

This morning, as they came into view, they were red.

Just like last time. But now it was all clear, all deserted.

So, thought George, I'll pull the throttle back, roar through the lights at 80 and show myself that last year everything was all right.

The grip round his waist, the weight on his shoulder, were stronger than ever. Even as his fingers started tuning the throttle he had an urge to look behind him. He fought it. The Suzuki leapt forward.

Last year it had been different. Now it came back clearly. Last year he had carried on through the lights, had too late seen a shape step off the pavement, had felt the shock of collision, fought to keep control, righted himself and roared away without looking back, leaving a huddled, bleeding bundle on the road for others to pick up later.

Without looking back. But now, a year later, the urge to look back was too great.

Only a snatched, split-second look as he turned his head. But what he saw was burned in his mind for the instant he had left to live. To his right he looked, straight into burning eyes set in a skull behind a helmet resting, weighing down on his shoulder. And he felt the grip of bony hands inside the gauntlets grip harder into his waist and an **inexorable** pull from behind. And he seemed to see a huddled bundle rise from the road behind him and a standing figure smiling with satisfaction.

At the inquest a verdict of 'misadventure' was passed. The deceased had lost control of his vehicle on the wet road: no blame could be attached to anyone. The coroner drew attention to the fact that two fatalities had occurred in the vicinity over the year before. Perhaps it could be classed as an accident 'black spot', though what hidden dangers could lurk in so innocent a stretch of suburban road quite defeated him.

---

inexorable: irresistibly strong

Digging for Trouble
Marilyn Watts

To whoever finds this:

I might not get to the end of this story. I might get murdered first. It all depends if Someone gets back from school before I get to the end. So I'm going to write it down quickly, OK? So that you can find it. I want someone to know what happened to me, Sam.

I hope you can read this. It's difficult, writing under here. But it seems the safest place. Trouble is, I can't hear things very well here. So it's not that safe. I need to know when the front door opens and the yelling, bag-waving terror of Doherty Road runs up the stairs and . . .

I'm wasting time, aren't I? Sorry.

It started this morning. First day back at school and you could see Dad was itching to get rid of us. He didn't exactly hang out the flags or kick us out of the front door, but I saw his reflection in the kitchen window and he was grinning. Great big grin. Almost rubbing his hands to get us out so that he could go back to his jewellery.

Dad and his jewellery. He makes it. (I've put that in just in case it's not Dad who finds this.) You'd think that someone who spends all day with tiny little fiddly things would be more careful. Wouldn't lose things? Would have a better idea of colour? Well, you'd be wrong, because . . .

Sorry. Back to the story.

First day back at school, and when we got there the teachers were walking around like zombies. Another year of having to put up with us lot. They all looked shellshocked. You know the look – it's as pleased as your parents' look on Christmas morning when you jump on their stomachs to wake them up and they groan and say something like 'it's only five o'clock, go away'. Anyway, Mrs French, our class teacher, looked like she wanted to say 'go away', but knew she couldn't. So she went all original (I don't think) and got us writing. Anything to keep us quiet.

'Write about something that happened during the holidays,' she said. We all groaned, but she pretended not to notice.

'What sort of thing, Miss?' Freddie asked. He's always asking stupid questions.

'Oh, anything. I know, Freddie . . .' Mrs F. suddenly seemed a bit brighter. '. . . tell me about something frightening – or funny.'

Well, that was that. I knew I wouldn't be able to write anything at all. Because nothing had happened during the summer. It wasn't like Alix, who went camping and woke the next morning to find there was a bull in the field. I didn't have a baby sister like Jim, who pulled down all the bags of sugar in Sainsbury's when their mother wasn't looking.

I looked at the blank paper and it looked back at me.

Everyone else was scribbling away.

'Sam . . .'

I glanced up. Mrs French was frowning. Warning. Better write something.

Something frightening. Something funny. On holiday.

And then I remembered. A doddle. Easy peasy. Watch me write!

There I was, scribbling away like everyone else. Something that happened. Yes! I'd even finish writing before break.

I thought I was writing a story.

I didn't realize it was my death warrant.

I wrote all about how we went on holiday, to the seaside. And how my parents thought up a Great Beach

Game to keep my sister happy. The game was Bury The Yellow Dolly. My sister's best dolly. My sister's very-favourite, mustn't-ever-lose, can't-get-to-sleep-without-it yellow dolly.

Mum and Dad buried the dolly, and my sister dug it up, giggling. They buried it again and she found it, one yellow leg sticking out of the yellow sand. They buried it, deeper, and she scrabbled around for a bit and finally found it, laughing.

Then my daft mum and dad went and buried the thing even deeper the next time. And they never, ever, found it again.

You wouldn't think you could lose something on a beach if you knew where you'd buried it, would you? But take it from me, you can. Very easily. Try it, next time you go to the seaside. But don't bury anything you care about.

My sister dug around, and couldn't find her doll. 'I'll help,' said Dad, casual-like. He started moving the sand aside, slowly at first, then faster and faster. Like a mole, or something trying to swim into the sand. Dad's face changed – you should have seen it. It went pink, then white, then a sort of grey colour. And when Mum realized what had happened she joined in too. Panic wasn't the word.

'We've got to find it,' she panted. 'We've *got* to.'

But they didn't.

I tried to help, but it was no good. I think the beach is just a thin layer of sand on top that looks as if it stays still, but underneath is a moving load of quicksand that takes things away on a conveyor belt and moves them around the beach.

My sister stopped giggling. She went very quiet, and then she started to cry. She howled and howled.

We went back to the hotel, and she was crying.

We had tea, and she was crying more.

Mum and Dad tried to put her to bed, and she was still howling.

That evening, Mum and Dad went back to the beach. They spent the whole night digging in the sand. They said it was really embarrassing. People kept walking along the road, calling down:

'Hey, aren't you two a bit old for that?'

'The worms'll be down towards the water, din ye know?'

'The sun's gone in, if you hadn't noticed.'

They came back with very bad tempers but no doll.

My sister cried for the rest of the holiday. The hotel got really fed up. They moved our table into another room, because it was putting people off their breakfast. My sister wouldn't go to bed, and every night Mum and Dad had to walk her up and down until she went to sleep.

The next day they went out and bought her another doll, but it wasn't Yellow Dolly so it didn't count. And then she realized that if she kept crying, she'd keep getting presents. So my sister cried every day for a week, and went home with four dolls, a panda, and a dead finger which glowed in the dark.

Now, I don't usually write things in class. And I've never written anything good. So it never occurred to me what could happen to my story.

After lunch, I went back into school and found a load of people gathered around the notice board, giggling and nudging each other. I went over and saw something surprising – my own writing staring back at me. I felt quite good, until I saw the heading. And noticed that the others had gone quiet and were watching me carefully.

I saw the story about my sister. Crying. For a dolly. Underneath a banner which said:

THIS SUMMER HOLIDAY

John pulled my sleeve. 'Her class went out and bought her a doll at lunchtime.'

Emma whispered, 'Joanne gave her a handkerchief in case she needed it to blow her nose.'

Someone else said, 'Jake Einsom told her to stop crying and she knocked him over.'

My life flashed in front of me.

I haven't told you about my sister, have I? She's called Janet at home, and Big Jan at school. I come up to her left shoulder. Her right shoulder's higher because of all the training she does for discus-throwing. And brother-throwing.

I might be older than her, but I'm smaller. A lot smaller. I haven't been the same size as her since the beach holiday. And that was seven years ago.

Was that the front door? It's difficult to tell, and I don't want to check, just in case.

It's very stuffy here. And cramped. But I like it.

I think I'll stay here for ever and ever.

Nightmare in Blue

Fredric Brown

He awoke to the brightest, bluest morning he had ever seen. Through the window beside the bed, he could see an almost incredible sky. George slid out of bed quickly, wide awake and not wanting to miss another minute of the first day of his vacation. But he dressed quietly so as not to awaken his wife. They had arrived here at the lodge – loaned them by a friend for the week of their vacation – late the evening before and Wilma had been very tired from the trip; he'd let her sleep as long as she could. He carried his shoes into the living room to put them on.

Tousle-haired little Tommy, their five-year-old, came out of the smaller bedroom he'd slept in, yawning. 'Want some breakfast?' George asked him. And when Tommy nodded, 'Get dressed then, and join me in the kitchen.'

George went to the kitchen but before starting breakfast, he stepped through the outside door and stood looking around; it had been dark when they'd arrived and he knew what the country was like only by description. It was virgin woodland, more beautiful than he'd pictured it. The nearest other lodge, he'd been told, was a mile away, on the other side of a fairly large lake. He couldn't see the lake for the trees but the path that started here from the kitchen door led to it, a little less than a quarter of a mile away. His friend had told him it was good for swimming, good for fishing. The swimming didn't interest George; he wasn't afraid of the water but he didn't like it either, and he'd never learned how to swim. But his wife was a good swimmer and so was Tommy – a regular little water rat, she called him.

Tommy joined him on the step; the boy's idea of getting dressed had been to put on a pair of swim trunks so that it hadn't taken him long. 'Daddy,' he said, 'let's go see the lake before we eat, huh, Daddy?'

'All right,' George said. He wasn't hungry himself and maybe when they got back Wilma would be awake.

The lake was beautiful, an even more intense blue than the sky, and smooth as a mirror. Tommy plunged into it gleefully and George called to him to stay where it was shallow, not to swim out.

'I can swim, Daddy. I can swim swell.'

'Yes, but your mother's not here. You stay close.'

'Water's *warm*, Daddy.'

Far out, George saw a fish jump. Right after breakfast he'd come down with his rod and see if he could catch a lunch for them.

A path along the edge of the lake led, he'd been told, to a place a couple of miles away where rowboats could be rented; he'd rent one for the whole week and keep it tied up here. He stared towards the end of the lake trying to see the place.

Suddenly, chillingly, there was an anguished cry, '*Daddy, my leg, it—*'

George whirled and saw Tommy's head way out, twenty yards at least, and it went under the water and came up again, but this time there was a frightening *glubbing* sound when Tommy tried to yell again. It must be cramp, George thought frantically; he'd seen Tommy swim several times that distance.

For a second he almost flung himself into the water, but then he told himself: It won't help him for me to drown with him and if I can get Wilma there's at least a chance . . .

He ran back towards the lodge. A hundred yards away he started yelling '*Wilma!*' at the top of his voice and when he was almost at the kitchen door she came through it, in pyjamas. And then she was running after him towards the lake, passing him and getting ahead since he was already winded, and he was fifty yards behind her when she reached the edge, ran into the water and swam strongly towards the spot where for a moment the back of the boy's head showed at the surface.

She was there in a few strokes and had him and then, as she put her feet down to tread water for the turn, he saw with sudden sheer horror – a horror mirrored in his wife's blue eyes – that she was standing on the bottom, holding their dead son, in only three feet of water.

Sting

Paul Groves and *Nigel Grimshaw*

Cyril Wicks leapt back from the hive. The bee had got under the net and stung him on the shoulder through his shirt. He was used to bee stings. He had probably been stung over a hundred times in his life as a beekeeper. But this sting really hurt; it was like toothache in the shoulder.

But in spite of the pain his eyes shone. He had done it. His work of the last few years had not been wasted: he had bred a big bee. There had been the careful selection of strains to get the biggest bee possible; and then the master stroke: feeding them on blood. He had tried both dried sheep's blood and horse's blood; both seemed effective.

He went inside to remove the sting. It was difficult but he got it out in two pieces. He placed them together; the sting measured two centimetres in length.

Down on his lonely Cornwall farm the chance of people getting stung was remote. He could go on and develop the bees. They would not go more than a mile or two from his hives in search of pollen. His nearest neighbour was four miles away. No one should know about it until he sold his secrets to a honey manufacturer. He envisaged bee farms with bees kept in giant sheds like the factory farming of pigs and cattle. It could make him rich and famous.

And that, with Cyril Wicks rich, could have been the end of the story. But his nearest neighbour was also experimenting. He was trying out different weed-killers to kill off some wild flowers that plagued one of his fields some two miles from Cyril Wicks' farm. The flowers seemed immune to normal weed-killer so he had mixed several brands together.

Unknown to both of them the bees had, one very hot day, taken pollen from the flowers of the treated plants. This caused a **mutation**.

Cyril Wicks had gone down to his hives some months later. He stopped and stared in amazement. There on top of one of the hives were three bees. They measured at least ten centimetres in length. Their bodies were as big as a blackbird's. As he went closer to look, he stepped on a twig. It snapped and frightened the bees which buzzed round him angrily and then came in immediately to the attack on the unfortunate Mr Wicks.

The first one stung him in the hand. He looked amazed as the sting went right through his palm and came out the other side. The second bee stung him like a red hot poker on the side of the knee. He collapsed to the ground and watched the third bee buzz over him. It did three circles and came in straight for his stomach. It drove its sting in deep. He twisted in agony for five minutes. Then he lay still.

mutation: physical change

There were no callers at the remote farm to discover the body. Only the postman called and he put his letters in a box at the end of the lane. It is assumed that the bees fed on the body as it decomposed, and sucked out the blood, as only his skeleton was found later.

For the bees developed a taste for the human body.

The first evidence the public of Cornwall had of the bees was the mysterious death of six cows and a sheep on the neighbouring farm. The vet could not understand the deaths and the giant stings measuring five centimetres.

It was while he was waiting for a report from London that some children saw the bees. They had travelled ten miles from Mr Wicks' farm to the coast. The children were dive-bombed while bathing. They were able to get into the water and frighten the bees away with splashing. At first the children's account was put down to exaggeration by their parents from London.

Then a tractor driver was found dead with a sting in his throat and half of the neck eaten away.

Nothing happened for the next few weeks but then the weather was very cold and dull.

On the first of June the town of Polven had just breakfasted. The milkmen and postmen were on their rounds; children were making their way to school; early morning shoppers were out. Then, from the south, came a faint hum. It was like a low note played on a cello. It got louder and louder. A policeman got off his bike and was looking up, expecting to see an aeroplane flying low. He suddenly saw this dark cloud. He took it at first to be a vast cloud of flies but soon he could see that it was a swarm of bees; not ordinary bees but giant bees following a queen. Before he could give any alarm they had passed over his head in the direction of the town centre. As they did so, they blotted out the sun. Being a brave man, he did not dive for cover but radioed his station.

At the police station they thought the officer was drunk and called him back off duty. But it would have made no difference if they had believed him; there was nothing they could do to stop what followed.

The bees flew straight to the centre of the town and settled on the town hall. Startled shoppers watched them crawl all over the building. They were hypnotized by the sight before attempting to escape from the area.

The bees might have stayed there round the queen but a car coming down the road back-fired. This startled the bees and they rose in an angry cloud and attacked everything that moved.

They buzzed down on cars and buses and any unfortunate pedestrians. Some shopkeepers did not get their doors closed quickly enough; office workers had windows open; so the bees were soon inside as well as out.

Thirty people were stung to death; a hundred were injured, some from crashing cars. Several old people died of fright.

Eventually, after an attack lasting fifteen minutes, the bees flew back to the town hall. The police called in the army who kept watch on the bees from armoured cars and tanks while the whole town was evacuated. This took all morning as old and sick people had to be moved by ambulance. All the time the worry was: Would the bees attack again?

At last it was done. Then crop-spraying planes and helicopters flew over the town and 'bombed' the bees with poisonous gas. The watchers from the tanks saw the bees drop off the town hall one by one.

Two weeks were given for the gas to clear. Then the bees were swept up in piles. Beekeepers of the area searched for the queen. She was not found. Had she escaped the gas?

A queen bee can lay up to three thousand eggs a day.

So far no sightings have been made of her. But then you can never be sure where a queen bee will find a hole or crevice to make a nest. The whole of Cornwall remains on the alert. Many of the inhabitants of Polven have not returned to their homes. The rest of the country does not sleep easily either.

Breakfast

James Herbert

The cold water trickled to a halt and the woman clucked her tongue. She twisted the tap off and placed the meagrely filled kettle on the electric stove. She left it to boil on the stone-cold ring.

Walking through to the hallway, the woman picked up the telephone receiver and flicked open the book lying beside it on the narrow hallstand. She found a number and dialled.

'I've already complained twice,' she said into the mouthpiece. 'Now the water's gone off completely. Why should I pay my water rates when I can't have bloody water?'

She flushed, angry with herself and the noiseless receiver. 'You've made me swear now, that's how angry I am,' she said. 'Don't give me any more excuses, I want someone round today to sort it out, otherwise I shall have to speak to your supervisor.'

Silence.

'What's that you say? You'll have to speak up.'

The phone remained dead.

'Yes, well, that's more like it. And I'll have you remember that **civility** costs nothing. I'll expect your man later this morning, then.'

The earpiece could have been a sea shell for all the noise it made.

'Right, thank you, and I hope it isn't necessary to call again.'

The woman allowed herself a *humph* of satisfaction as she replaced the receiver.

---

civility: politeness

'I don't know what this country's coming to,' she said, pulling her unkempt cardigan tight around her as a breeze – a warm breeze – flowed down from the stairway. She went back into the kitchen.

As she rinsed the teapot with water from the cold kettle, the woman complained to her husband seated at the pine kitchen table, newspaper propped up against the empty milk bottle before him. A fly, its body thick and black and as big as a bee, landed on the man's cheek and trekked across the pallid landscape. The man ignored it.

'. . . not even as though water's cheap nowadays,' his wife droned. 'We have to pay rates even when it's off. Should never have been allowed to split from normal rates – it was just their way of bumping up prices. Like everything else, I suppose, money, money, it rules everything. I dread doing the monthly shop. God knows how much everything's gone up since last time. Afraid you'll have to give me more housekeeping soon, Barry. Yes, I know, but I'm sorry. If you want to eat the way you're used to, you'll have to give me more.'

She stirred the tea and quickly sucked her finger when cold water splashed and burned it. Putting the lid on the teapot, she took it over to the kitchen table and sat opposite her husband.

'Tina, are you going to eat those cornflakes or just sit and stare at them all day?'

Her daughter did not even shrug.

'You'll be late for playschool again if you don't get a move on. And how many times have I told you Cindy isn't allowed at the table? You spend more time speaking to that doll than you do eating.'

She scooped up the dolly that she, herself, had placed in her daughter's lap only minutes before and propped it up on the floor against a table leg. Tina began to slide off her chair.

The mother jumped and pulled the child erect again, tutting as she did so. Tina's small chin rested against her chest and the woman tried vainly to lift it.

'All right, you go ahead and sulk, see where it gets you.'

A small creature with many eyelash legs stirred from its nest in the little girl's ear. It crawled out and scuttled into the dry white hair of the child's scalp.

The woman poured the tea, the water colourless, black specks that were the unbrewed tea leaves collecting in the strainer to form a soggy mould. Silverfish scattered from beneath the milk jug as she lifted it and unsuccessfully tried to pour the clots of sour cream into the cups.

'Sammy, you stop that chattering and finish your toast. And will you put your school tie on straight, how many more times do I have to tell you? At ten years of age you think you'd be old enough to dress yourself properly.'

Her son silently gazed at the green bread beside his bowl of cornflakes, the cereal stirring gently as small creatures fed beneath. He was grinning, a ventriloquist's dummy, cheek muscles tightened by shrinkage. A misty film clouded his eyes, a spoon balanced ungripped in his clawed hand. A length of string around his chest tied him to the chair.

The woman sipped the tasteless tea and, with an impatient hand, flicked at the flies buzzing around Tina's head. Her husband's pupil-less stare from the other side of the table irritated her, too, the whites of his eyes showing between half-closed lids.

'What shall we do this morning, everyone?' she asked, forgetting it was both a work and school day. 'A walk to the park? The rain's finally stopped, you know. My goodness, I thought it never would, didn't you, Barry? Must do some shopping later, but I think we could manage a little walk first, take advantage of the weather, hmn? What do you say, Sammy? You could take your roller skates. Yes, you too, Tina, I wasn't forgetting you. Perhaps the cinema later. No, don't get excited – I want you to finish your breakfast first.'

She leaned across and patted her daughter's little clenched fist.

'It'll be just like old times, won't it?' Her voice became a whisper, and the words were slow. 'Just like old times.'

Tina slid down in her chair once more and this time disappeared beneath the table.

'That's right, dear, you look for Cindy, she can come to the park too. Anything interesting in the news today, Barry? Really, oh good gracious, people are *funny*, aren't they? Makes you wonder what the world's coming to, just what on earth you'll read next. Manners, *Samuel*, hand before mouth.'

She scraped away surface mould from a drooping slice of bread and bit into it. 'Don't let your tea get cold, pet,' she lightly scolded her husband, Barry. 'You've got all day to read the newspaper. I think I'll have a lie-down in a little while; I'm not feeling too well today. Think I've got flu coming on.'

The woman glanced towards the shattered window, a warm breeze ruffling the thin hair straggling over her forehead. She saw but did not perceive the nuclear-wasted city outside.

Her attention drifted back to her family once more and she watched the black fly, which had fully explored the surface of her husband's face by now, disappearing into the gaping hole of his mouth.

She frowned, and then she sighed. 'Oh, Barry,' she said, 'you're not just going to sit there all day again, are you?'

Tiny, glittering tear beads formed in the corners of each eye, one brimming over leaving a jerky silver trail down her chin. Her family didn't even notice.

The Hand That Feeds Me
Michael Z. Lewin

It was one of those sultry summer evenings, warm and humid and hardly any wind. The sun was just going down and I was grazing the alleys downtown, not doing badly. It never ceases to amaze me the quantity of food that human beings throw away. Especially in warm weather. The only real problem about getting a decent meal is the competition.

When I saw a man poking in a barrel I said to myself, 'Here's trouble.' I was wrong, but I was right.

The old guy was grazing too and at first he didn't notice me. But when he did, though I couldn't make out the words, he was obviously friendly. And then he threw me a piece of meat.

It's not always smart to take meat from strange men, but this guy seemed genuine enough. I checked the meat out carefully, and then I ate it. It was good. Topped me up nicely.

I stayed with the old guy for a while, and we got along. I'd root a bit, he'd root a bit. And we'd move elsewhere.

Then he settled down to go to sleep. He patted the sacking, inviting me to sleep too, but it was early so I moved on.

A couple of hours later it was semi-dark, like it gets in the town. I didn't go back down the old guy's alley on purpose. Things just worked out that way. There are forces in a town at night. They push you this way, they push you that.

I could tell immediately that something was wrong. I approached cautiously, but nothing happened. Nothing could happen. The old guy was dead.

There was blood on his face. There was blood on his clothes. Someone had given him a terrible beating. Beatings are something I know about.

I licked one of the wounds. The blood was dry on top, but still runny under the crust. The old guy's body was pretty warm. Whatever had happened wasn't long over.

Nosing around, I picked up the scents of three different men. They were all fresh, hanging in the tepid air. Three men together, three against one. One old man. That could not be right.

I set out after them.

They had headed away from downtown. Curiously, they had stuck to the alleys, these three men, though they hadn't stopped at any of the places I would have. The places my dead acquaintance would have.

The only time I had trouble finding the **spoor** was where the alley crossed a street near a couple of stores. Seems they went into one of the stores, then headed back for the alley.

After another block I began to find beer cans they had handled.

At first I picked each can up, carefully, and I put it where I could find it again. But once I had one can from each of the men, I ignored the rest. I followed the trail with increasing confidence. I figured I knew where they were going.

The long, narrow park by the river is popular on a summer's night. I could tell immediately that it was teeming with life, and not just because so many scents crossed that of the trio I was following. All you have to do is listen. A dozen human beings, not to mention the other creatures.

---

spoor: scent of the men

But my trio made it easy again. They were down by the riverside, whooping and hollering and throwing things into the water.

I was extremely cautious as I drew close. I wasn't quite sure what I would do. I only knew that I would do something.

I saw them clearly enough. Young, boisterous men, rough with each other and loud. They picked up stones and swung thick sticks to hit the stones into the river. Already drunk and unsteady, most of the time they missed, but when one connected they would all make a terrible din to celebrate the crack of stick on stone.

Lying on the grass behind them were more cans of beer and a pile of jackets. There was also a fire. A fire! On a hot night like this.

It wasn't until I crept near that I realized that in the fire they had been burning something belonging to the old man. The old man who gave me meat. The old man they had beaten to death.

I was sorely tempted to sink my teeth into the nearest one, maybe push him over the bank and into the water. But I was self-disciplined. A ducking was too good for these three, these murderers.

I edged close to the fire, to the beer cans. To the jackets.

The idea was to grab all three garments, but just as I made my move, one of the louts happened to turn round and see me in the light from the embers.

He yelled ugly things to his friends, and they reeled back towards me. I am not a coward but they did have sticks. And I am considerably bigger than a stone.

I grabbed the top jacket and ran for it.

They chased for a while, but they were no match for me running full out, even lugging the flapping jacket. And this was no small, lightweight thing. It was heavy, leather, and not clean.

But I got 'clean' away, and the last I heard of the three young killers was what I took for loud, angry swearing as it floated across the humid night air.

I went straight back to the body of the old man. I laid the jacket down by one of his hands and pushed a sleeve as best I could into its forceless grasp. I spread the jacket out.

I left the old man three more times. After each trip I returned with a beer can. Each can reeked of a killer. Other men might not be able to track them from the smell, but each of the cans bore a murderer's finger marks.

Then I sat and rested. I didn't know what it would look like from higher up, but from where I sat the scene looked as if the old man had grabbed the jacket of one of the men who had attacked him. Beer-drunk men. The old man had grasped and wouldn't let go. They, cowards that they were, ran off.

Cowards that they were, if one of them was brought to justice from his jacket, he would squeal on the other two from his pack.

I was pleased with my justice.

I raised my eyes to the moon, and I cried for the dead man. I cried and cried until I heard living men near the alley open their doors. Until I heard them come out into the still summer night. Until I heard them make their way to the alley to see what the fuss was.

Once I was sure they were doing that, I set off into the darkness.

Dog, Cat, and Baby
Joe R. Lansdale

Dog did not like Baby. For that matter, Dog did not like Cat. But Cat had claws – sharp claws.

Dog had always gotten attention. Pat on head. 'Here, boy, here's a treat. Nice dog. Good dog. Shake hands. Speak! Sit. Nice dog.'

Now there was Baby.

Cat had not been a problem, really.

Cat was liked, not loved by family. They petted Cat sometimes. Fed her. Did not mistreat her. But they did not love her. Not way they loved Dog – before Baby.

Damn little pink thing that cried.

Baby got 'Oooohs and Ahhhs.' When Dog tried to get close to Masters, they say, 'Get back, boy. Not *now.*'

When would it be *now*?

Dog never see now. Always Baby get now. Dog get nothing. Sometimes they so busy with Baby it be all day before Dog get fed. Dog never gets treats anymore. Could not remember last pat on head or 'Good Dog!'

Bad business. Dog not like it.

Dog decide to do something about it.

Kill Baby. Then there be Dog, Cat again. They not love Cat, so things be okay.

Dog thought that over. Wouldn't take much to rip little Baby apart. Baby soft, pink. Would bleed easy.

Baby often put in Jumper that hung between doorway when Master Lady hung wash. Baby be easy to get then.

So Dog waited.

One day Baby put in Jumper and Master Lady go outside to hang wash. Dog looks at pink thing jumping, thinks about ripping to pieces. Thinks on it long and hard. Thought makes him so happy his mouth drips water. Dog starts toward Baby, making fine moment last.

Baby looks up, sees Dog coming toward it slowly, almost creeping. Baby starts to cry.

But before Dog can reach Baby, Cat jumps.

Cat been hiding behind couch.

Cat goes after Dog, tears Dog's face with teeth, with claws. Dog bleeds, tries to run. Cat goes after him.

Dog turns to bite.

Cat hangs claw in Dog's eye.

Dog yelps, runs.

Cat jumps on Dog's back, biting Dog on top of head.

Dog tries to turn corner into bedroom. Cat, tearing at him with claws, biting with teeth, makes Dog lose balance. Dog running very fast, fast as he can go, hits the edge of doorway, stumbles back, falls over.

Cat gets off Dog.

Dog lies still.

Dog not breathing.

Cat knows Dog is dead. Cat licks blood from claws, from teeth with rough tongue.

Cat has gotten rid of Dog.

Cat turns to look down hall where Baby is screaming.

Now for *other* one.

Cat begins to creep down hall.

Well, Well, Well
Kate Hall

'Well you obviously can't keep it.'

'What do you mean, CAN'T keep it? Who says I can't?'

'It's obvious – you'll have to have an abortion.'

'I don't want an abortion. I want to . . .'

'You can't, just think about it for a minute.'

'I have thought about it, I've thought about it a lot.'

'But you've just started college.'

'I know I've started college but there's a crèche there.'

'Oh, I see, you're going to go in pregnant and have the baby in between lectures.'

'It's due in the holidays and anyway I can get time off, other people have done it before, you know.'

'That doesn't mean you have to, though, does it? And what about money?'

'I'll manage.'

'What, on a grant, with a baby and no father?'

'Yes, on a grant, with a baby and no father – that's what's really worrying you, isn't it? Bloody hell, in this day and age!'

'Well it would help if you would say who the father is, or don't you know?'

'Of course I know, but I don't want him to.'

'Why not for Christ's sake, he ought to pay for it – you could get maintenance you know or he could pay for an abortion.'

'I don't want him to pay for anything and I am NOT having an abortion.'

'He's not married is he?'

'No, he's not married.'

'Then I don't see . . .'

'I just don't want anyone interfering, that's all.'

'Well you needn't worry on my account – I'm not having anything to do with it and don't expect me to baby-sit either.'

'No one asked you to.'

'Not yet, but just you wait. Honestly, I thought YOU were old enough to know better. It's embarrassing.'

'You'll be saying "What will the neighbours say?" next.'

'I don't give a damn about the neighbours but they will think things if there's no father.'

'There is a father!'

'Oh yes, an anonymous one.'

'I KNOW who he is.'

'Well at least tell me.'

'No. Look, I made a decision, I got pregnant on purpose. I want to have this baby, okay?'

'BUT MUM – at your age!'

Reunion
Arthur C. Clarke

People of Earth, do not be afraid. We come in peace – and why not? For we are your cousins; we have been here before.

You will recognize us when we meet, a few hours from now. We are approaching the solar system almost as swiftly as this radio message. Already, your Sun dominates the sky ahead of us. It is the Sun our ancestors and yours shared ten million years ago. We are men, as you are; but you have forgotten your history, while we have remembered ours.

We colonized Earth, in the reign of the great reptiles, who were dying when we came and whom we could not save. Your world was a tropical planet then, and we felt it would make a fair home for our people. We were wrong. Though we were masters of space, we knew so little about climate, about evolution, about genetics . . .

For millions of summers – there were no winters in those ancient days – the colony flourished. Isolated though it had to be, in a universe where the journey from one star to the next takes years, it kept in touch with its parent civilization. Three or four times in every century, starships would call and bring news of the galaxy.

But two million years ago, Earth began to change. For ages it had been a tropical paradise; then the temperature fell, and the ice began to creep down from the poles. As the climate altered, so did the colonists. We realize now that it was a natural adaptation to the end of the long summer, but those who had made Earth their home for so many generations believed that they had been attacked by a strange and repulsive disease. A disease that did not kill, that did no physical harm – but merely disfigured.

Yet some were immune; the change spared them and their children. And so, within a few thousand years, the colony had split into two separate groups – almost two separate species – suspicious and jealous of each other.

The division brought envy, discord, and, ultimately, conflict. As the colony disintegrated and the climate steadily worsened, those who could do so withdrew from Earth. The rest sank into **barbarism**.

We could have kept in touch, but there is so much to do in a universe of a hundred trillion stars. Until a few years ago, we did not know that any of you had survived. Then we picked up your first radio signals, learned your simple languages, and discovered that you had made the long climb back from savagery. We come to greet you, our long-lost relatives – and to help you.

We have discovered much in the **eons** since we abandoned Earth. If you wish us to bring back the eternal summer that ruled before the Ice Ages, we can do so. Above all, we have a simple remedy for the offensive yet harmless genetic plague that afflicted so many of the colonists.

Perhaps it has run its course – but if not, we have good news for you. People of Earth, you can rejoin the society of the universe without shame, without embarrassment.

If any of you are still white, we can cure you.

---

barbarism: primitive savagery
eons: long ages

Starbride
Anthony Boucher

I always knew, ever since we were in school together, that he'd love me some day; and I knew somehow too that I'd always be in second place. I didn't really care either, but I never guessed then what I'd come second to: a native girl from a conquered planet.

I couldn't guess because those school days were before the Conquest and the Empire, back in the days when we used to talk about a rocket to a moon and never dreamed how fast it would all happen after that rocket.

When it did all begin to happen I thought at first what I was going to come second to was Space itself. But that wasn't for long and now Space can never take him away from me and neither can she, not really, because she's dead.

But he sits there by the waters and talks and I can't even hate her, because she was a woman too, and she loved him too, and that was what she died of.

He doesn't talk about it as often as he used to, and I suppose that's something. It's only when the fever's bad, or he's tried to talk to the Federal Council again about a humane colonial policy. That's worse than the fever.

He sits there and he looks up at her star and he says, 'But damn it, they're *people*. Oh, I was like all the rest at first; I was expecting some kind of monster even after the reports from the Conquest troops. And when I saw that they looked almost like us, and after all those months in the space ship, with the old regulation against mixed crews . . .'

He has to tell it. The psychiatrist explained that to me very carefully. I'm only glad it doesn't come so often now.

'Everybody in Colonial Administration was doing it,' he says. 'They'd pick the girl that came closest to somebody back home and they'd go through the Vlnian marriage rite – which of course isn't recognized legally under the CA, at least not where we're concerned.'

I've never asked him whether she came close to me.

'It's a beautiful rite, though,' he says. 'That's what I keep telling the Council: Vln had a much higher level of pre-Conquest civilization than we'll admit. She taught me poetry and music that . . .'

I know it all by heart now. All the poetry and all the music. It's strange and sad and like nothing you ever dreamed of . . . and like everything you ever dreamed.

'It was living with her that made me know,' he says. 'Being with her, part of her, knowing that there was nothing grotesque, nothing monstrous about green flesh and white in the same bed.'

No, that's what he used to say. He doesn't say that part any more. He does love me. 'They've got to understand!' he says, looking at her star.

The psychiatrist explained how he's transferring his guilt to the Council and the Colonial policy; but I still don't see why he has to have guilt. He couldn't help it. He wanted to come back. He meant to come back. Only that was the trip he got space fever, and of course after that he was planet-bound for life.

'She had a funny name,' he says. 'I never could pronounce it right – all vowels. So I called her Starbride, even though she said that was foolish – we both belonged to the same star, the Sun, even if we were of different planets. Now is that a primitive reaction? I tell you the average level of Vlnian scientific culture . . .'

And I still think of it as her star when he sits there and looks at it. I can't keep things like that straight, and he does call her Starbride.

'I swore to come back before the child was born,' he said. 'I swore by her God and by mine and He heard me under both names. And she said very simply, "If you don't, I'll die." That's all, just "I'll die." And then we drank native wine and sang folksongs all night and went to bed in the dawn.'

And he doesn't need to tell me about his letter to her, but he does. He doesn't need to because I sent it myself. It was the first thing he thought of when he came out of the fever and saw the calendar and I wrote it down for him and sent it. And it came back with the CA stamp: *Deceased* and that was all.

'And I don't know how she died,' he says, 'or even whether the child was born. Try to find out anything about a native from a Colonial Administrator! They've got to be made to realize . . .'

Then he usually doesn't talk for a while. He just sits there by the waters and looks up at the blue star and sings their sad folksongs with the funny names: *Saint Louis Blues* and *Barbara Allen* and *Lover, Come Back To Me.*

And after a while I say, 'I'm not planet-bound. Some day when you're well enough for me to leave you I'll go to Vln—'

'"*Earth*",' he says, almost as though it was a love-word and not just a funny noise. 'That's their name for Vln. She called herself an Earth woman, and she called me her Martian.'

'I'll go to Earth,' I say, only I can never pronounce it quite right and he always laughs a little, 'and I'll find your child and I'll bring it back to you.'

Then he turns and smiles at me and after a while we leave the waters of the canal and go inside again away from her blue star. Those are the times when I can almost endure the pain of being second in his heart, second to a white Starbride far away and dead on a planet called Earth.

Sticks and Stones
Annii Miethke

'Four Eyes! Freckle!' That hardly bruised.

'Beachball!'

Nola had always been a large girl. No, too **scant** a word. Honestly? Fat! Nola had always been fat. At six months, she was an unsightly globe of bulging tyres, creases and dimples.

'She's only a baby, Eileen. She'll grow out of it. You'll see.'

That done-to-death assurance to Nola's mother proved partly accurate, for Nola did grow out, but not 'of it'. At age four, thirty-five kilos, galumphing steps as wide as they were long at five; and at six, school.

'Fatty Fatty Boom Sticks!'

'Nola, you are as big as a house!' Delighted giggles.

'Nola in the middle!' Exultant shrieks. 'Piggy!'

Her very early school years, Nola was not overly distressed by these jibes. Willy was 'Smelly', Sarah 'Carrot', Brett 'Bugs'. They all wanted to be someone. Nola was almost delighted at the attention she received. Popularity.

Tick . . . Tick . . . but the kids did not grow wiser. They did not outlive their childish ploys.

'Nola doesn't even fit in the middle anymore!'

Almost friendly kiddy-teases evolved into youngsters' taunts. Meant. Persecution, mockery, jeers. The guffaws! They all developed and continued, increasing, cruelly cutting.

But oh, Nola bore it well, so well . . . at least in front of the others. Alone and the tear-currents, the grief, and the twisting agonizing knife. She was a lonely, friendless child; a melted pat of butter.

---

scant: weak

Taunts more clever. They knew their similes and metaphors.

'Next week you are all to bring your swimming costumes.'

Mr Coleman's swimming instructions continued.

Nola's fear **escalated**.

'Does one inhale or exhale, that is, breathe in or out when attempting to float on the water?' Several moments of silence ensued, Mr Coleman impressed that the children were rationalizing it out.

Her striped, coloured dress caught Peter's eye.

'Beachballs float, don't they, sir?'

'Yes.'

'Why, then, just grab on to Nola!'

And that was it! That was the first time everybody applauded.

From then it snowballed. Insults and taunts cascaded, laughs, cheers, always applause; eroding, until Nola could weather little more and became a skeletal personality lost in hand. A mere twelve.

Exaggerated? Ha! You obviously don't know.

Suicide contemplated. Too extreme? Perhaps not . . .

The next week for gym, Nola brought no swimming costume. That raised the house. The following week, Nola brought no Nola. Each gym day, she went to the dentist, she was sick, her mother was sick. Absences increased.

Gym day changed, and their joke was not to tell Nola.

'No!' she shrieked, fully clothed, 'I won't . . .' She screamed, seeing the mocking wet hands of the water reaching up for her, and aware of those at her back. She would not allow them the satisfaction of seeing the bobbing beachball in action.

---

escalated: mounted

. . . definitely not. Pills, knife, razor, gun, drowning . . . ?
She unpegged the others, leaving her last notion hanging
dankly on her mind-line.

No, Peter, correction. Beachballs do not float. Not
always. Blown up they will, but pierce the smallest hole (it
doesn't have to be a whopping gash!) and they 'piffff',
down, flat, gurgle, **pendulate**, falling. They sink. If all their
air escapes, they sink. Why couldn't you see that?

Willy didn't smell (he never *really* had), Sarah used
dye, Brett had braces. Nola had a **genetic disorder**. What
could *she* do? In desperation she wore glasses, walked
pigeon-toed, did all she could to her appearance in the
hope of changing the source of their taunts. But 'Four
Eyes!' was nothing. No torment surpassed that of
'Beachball'! They knew it and she felt it. It lent itself so
well to numerous, humorous taunts, particularly since
theirs was a coastal town.

Nola was fast becoming a beachball-wreck, washed up
on deserted sands. She was only fourteen . . . Perhaps
she would.

'Yeah, and I'm inviting all the good-lookers. I wanna
play around with some girls.' That was Peter.

'You wanna play around, so you'll be inviting Nola!'

'I'm not having a beach party!'

Peals of laughter and cheers. Everybody applauded.

. . . Perhaps she *really* would.

The remaining dribble of air finally escaped. Her
resistance gave. There was to be a fancy dress day at
school the following Monday. What was Nola to come as?

Rhetorical.

She neither shrieked nor screamed.

---

pendulate: swinging
genetic disorder: inherited illness
rhetorical: question needing no answer, asked for effect

But come Monday, come no Nola; come Tuesday, come no Nola; come the following Monday, the following week . . . month . . . came Nola nowhere.

. . . Perhaps she did.

She had become a beachball-wreck washed up on the deserted sands.

She did.

Nobody applauded.

The Bridge
Jessie Kesson

For the first time in his eight years, he had caught the biggest tiddler. A **beezer** it was. Even Mike – the tiddler champ – grudgingly admitted its superiority.

'But maybe it's the jam jar that makes it look so big,' Mike qualified.

'Some kinds of glass makes things look bigger.'

It *wasn't* the glass that made it look bigger. He had urged Mike to look inside the jam jar. And there swam surely – the king of tiddlers.

'*I* don't reckon it much.'

Anxious to keep on Mike's side, Titch McCabe peered into the jar. 'And Mungrel doesn't reckon it much either. Do you Mung?'

Mungrel, who never spoke until somebody else put words into his mouth, agreed with Titch. 'S'right. I don't reckon it much neither.'

'Could easy not be a tiddler at *all*!'

Dave Lomax shouted from his perch on the branch of the tree. 'Could just be a trout. A wee trout!'

'– Could be . . .' Mung echoed; for although he had never set eyes on a trout he was in agreement with the others to 'disqualify' the tiddler.

'Let's *go* men!' Mike commanded. Suddenly tiring of the discussion.

'Scarper! First to reach the chain bridge is the *greatest*!'

'You're not some kind of wee trout.' He protested. Running to catch up with them.

'You're *not* . . .'

---

beezer: whopper

He stopped running to peer into his jam jar to reassure its occupant.

'You're a *tiddler*. And you're the *biggest* tiddler we've caught the day.'

'*Hold* it, men!' he shouted to the others. 'Wait for me.'

The authority in his voice surprised himself. Usually he was content enough to lag behind the others. Tolerated by them, because he was handy for doing all the things they didn't like to do themselves. Like swiping his big brother's fag ends. And ringing the bell of the school caretaker's door. Or handing over his pocket money to 'make up the odds' for a bottle of '**juice**'. But *today* he was one of them. He had caught the biggest tiddler.

It was when he caught up with them at the bridge that his newly found feeling of triumph began to desert him.

'OK tiddler champ,' Mike said.

'Gi' us the jar. We'll guard the tiddler.'

'Yeah. Give,' Mung echoed.

'It's *your* turn to span the bridge,' Dave said.

He grasped his jar firmly against his anorak. He didn't need anybody to guard his tiddler. He didn't want to span the bridge either! *Nobody* spanned the bridge until they were *ten* at least! The others had never before expected *him* to span the bridge. He had always raced across it – the safe way – keeping guard over all the tiddlers while the others spanned it.

'*Your* turn,' Mike was insisting. '*We* have spanned it. Hundreds of times.'

'*Thousands* of times!' Dave amended.

'Even *Mungrel* spans it,' Titch reminded him. 'Don't you Mung? And Mungrel's even titchier than me!'

'Mungrel's *eleven*,' he pointed out. 'I'm not even nine yet.'

'Only . . . Mungrel's not *chicken*!' Mike said, 'Are you,

---

juice: lemonade

Mung? You're not chicken.'

'I'm not chicken *neither*!' he protested. 'I'm *not* chicken.'

'OK! OK!' they said. Beginning to close in on him. 'OK! So you're not chicken! . . . *Prove* it . . . just prove it . . . that's *all*! Span the bridge and *prove* it.'

He knew how to span the bridge all right. Sometimes – sometimes kidding on that he was only 'mucking around' he practised a little. Spanning the part of the bridge that stood above the footpath. Knowing that even if he fell he would still be safe – safe as he felt *now*. Knowing that the ground was under his dangling legs.

Left hand over right – left over right – all his fear seemed to have gone into his hands. All his mind's urgings could scarcely get them to keep their grip of the girder.

Left over right – left over –

The river's bank was beneath him now. Dark pools flowed under the bank, he remembered. Pools where the tiddlers often hid – the *biggest* tiddlers. Sometimes he had caught them just sitting bent forward on the bank. Holding his jam jar between his legs. His bare feet scarcely touching the water. He'd felt afraid then, too. A *different* kind of fear. Not for himself. Just of things which his eyes couldn't see. But which his hands could feel. Things that brushed against them . . . Grasping and slimy.

He would never have been surprised, if, when he brought up his jam jar to examine its contents, he discovered neither tiddler nor tadpole inside it, but some strange creature, for which nobody had yet found a name.

Left over – right – left –

The shallows were beneath him now. Looking, even from this height, as safe as they had always looked. His *feet* had always told him how safe the shallows were. A safety – perfect in itself – because it was **intensified** by surrounding danger.

---

intensified: heightened

You could stand, he remembered, with one foot in the shallows, your toes curling round the small stones. While your other foot sank into the sand – down and down . . .

Left over right, left over right – over –

He had a feeling that his body would fall away from his arms and hands long before he reached the end of the bridge.

Left over right – over.

It might be easier that way. Easier just to drop down into the water. And leave his hands and arms clinging to the bridge. All by themselves.

Left over – right.

He was at the middle of the river now. That part of it which they said had no bottom. That could be *true*, he realized. Remembering how, when they skimmed their stones across the water, into the middle, the stones would disappear. But you could never hear them *sound* against the depths into which they fell.

Mike had once said that, though the water *looked* as

quiet as anything – far down, where you couldn't see, it just kept whirling round, and round, waiting to suck anybody at all down inside it . . .

– over – right – left –

He wouldn't look down again. He wouldn't look down *once*. He would count up to fifty. The way he always counted to himself – when bad things were about to happen.

One two three four five six . . . Better to count in tens, he wouldn't lose his 'place' so easily that way—

One . . . two . . . three . . . four . . . five . . . six seven eight.

He thought he could hear the voices of the others. He must be past the middle of the bridge, now – the water beneath him was still black but he could see shapes within it.

The voices were coming nearer. He knew they were *real*.

'CHARGE! MEN!' Mike was shouting. 'CHARGE!'

He could hear them **reeshling** up the river bank. And their feet clanking along the footpath. They were running away . . . Ever since he could remember the days had ended with them all running away. Only *this* time, his tiddler would be with them too. And Mike would boast that *he* had catched it. He had almost forgotten about the tiddler. And it no longer seemed to matter.

Green and safe, the bank lay below him. He could jump down now. But he wouldn't. Not yet! It was only titches like Mungrel, that leapt down from the girder, the moment they saw the bank beneath them.

Mike never did that. He could see, clear as anything in his mind's eye, how Mike always finished spanning the bridge, one hand clinging to the girder, the other gesturing, high, for a clear runway for himself before swooping down to earth again with cries of triumph!

'*Bat* Man! *Bat* Man!'

---

reeshling: crashing (Scottish dialect)

Teachers!
Jane Morley

The teacher bit my head off on Monday, for being late. I tried explaining how I'd helped Adele to the ambulance because she'd broken her leg.

'Couldn't she have hopped there herself?' the teacher exclaimed.

On Tuesday I was late again.

'My house burned down,' I told her.

'After calling the fire brigade, there was no need to be late for school,' she replied. 'The next latecomer will wipe the tables after lunch.'

On Wednesday, the teacher's house burned down. Escaping, she broke her leg. She didn't turn up for school.

I left the cloth on her desk.

Soldier
Ben Rayner

As he drove along, sweat poured off his pulsating brow. He saw the helicopters in his rear-view mirror; they darted like vultures waiting for a death to feed upon. His heart ran riot and he looked in the mirror again; he could see the helicopters drawing closer. The nearer they drew, the more certain his death became. Then all about him were flames.

The next morning, newspapers showed a burnt-out lorry with a charred body at the wheel. A man chewing his morning toast and reading the paper said:

'Bloody Iraqi soldier, glad he's dead.'

Court Martial
Charles C. O'Connell

He stood pallid and tense before the officers. Though he was now unarmed and shorn of all his field equipment, his tunic seemed to drag heavily on his shoulders, and the weight of his helmet was almost unbearable; he could hardly keep his head erect. His right arm, which had been twisted viciously behind his back, hung limply by his side, numb and lifeless, except for the faint pulse that beat under his armpit.

He stood with his feet apart, although years of discipline urged him to stand to attention, but he knew that if he did so he would topple over. In fact, it made no difference how he presented himself; the verdict of the court martial would be 'guilty'. He had disobeyed orders. Only his conscience could justify his action. According to their code, he was a rebel . . . Well, let it be. If he had to relive the episode, he would do exactly the same thing.

The heat inside was quite intolerable. He longed to step back a little into the current of air that moved the canvas by the door, yet he dared not. Such an action might **antagonize** his judges even more, and although he could see no **vestige** of mercy or even humanity in their stern faces, he had hope that perhaps, in spite of everything, they would understand.

'You have heard the evidence.' The voice of his superior officer jarred on his ears. 'Have you anything to say?'

The prisoner thought for a moment. Had he anything to say in his defence? No, he had not – nothing that they

antagonize: annoy, make hostile
vestige: a small trace

could understand. But what could he not say of this useless bloodshed, which was for assassins rather than soldiers! This war on women and innocent children was repugnant to him. Nothing, he thought, could justify this mass murder, yet to say so here would be treason.

'Answer!' snarled the officer.

'I have nothing to say.'

'Do you deny that you allowed those refugees through?'

Perhaps it would be better if he said something – anything to shorten the farcical trial. 'I let them through,' he said hoarsely, admitting the charge for the first time.

The officer smiled. 'Against your specific orders?'

'Yes.'

Why in the name of glory did they persist in this mockery?

The two officers held a whispered consultation. One of the guards behind the prisoner shuffled for an instant and was still again. Then the second officer spoke. His was a soft face with none of the harsh lines of his superior, but his eyes were colder than a winter dawn.

'We should be interested to know why you allowed all three to go. Had you done your duty by one, there would have been no further trouble. Were they friends of yours? Did you know them? Or were you tempted by the amount of the bribe?'

The prisoner shook his head, and the perspiration temporarily held by his eyebrows trickled to his chin. 'They offered no bribe, sir. I did not know them.'

'Then why did you let them through?'

'I thought it was – just.'

'What do you know of justice?' the officer sneered.

The prisoner closed his eyes. Once again the picture of those three weary travellers came to his mind. They were fleeing from a terror which he represented. He had not harmed them because they looked so desperately tired, or perhaps it had been that heart-searching appeal in the young woman's eyes, or perhaps it was because of the child, so helpless in a world gone mad . . . Whatever the reason, his orders had suddenly appeared monstrously evil.

He opened his eyes. 'I am a soldier,' he said firmly. 'I will not become an assassin.'

And the guard behind him struck him at the base of the neck and he slumped to the ground. He was vaguely conscious of being kicked, but it did not hurt any more. A strange sense of unreality possessed him, as though he existed only in a dream.

Some time later, he found himself on his feet again. The business of the court had finished. There had been no death sentence. One of the officers merely nodded his head to the guard, and the prisoner was propelled towards the door.

He staggered as he came into the sunlight, and his helmet fell off. Nobody picked it up – he would have no further use for it. The cool air stirring through his matted hair was as invigorating as wine. He was rushed forward and then, some paces from the door behind a high, screening boulder, his guards stopped.

The prisoner was under no illusion. He knew that in a few moments he would be dead. Yet he had no regrets. Perhaps it would be better to leave this world of injustice and suffering.

Vaguely, he wondered if it would always be like this. That could hardly be possible. Men must one day realize the futility of bloodshed. Perhaps, in a thousand or two thousand years, men would have at last learnt to live in peace and there would be no greed, nor wars, nor murder.

He stood erect. He did not feel afraid. He was filled with a strange, new hope. He thought of those three travel-stained refugees. He hoped they got through to Egypt. Once there, the child would be safe from Herod's barbarous assassins . . .

The Aqueduct
Ray Bradbury

It leapt over the country in great stone arches. It was empty now, with the wind blowing in its sluices; it took a year to build, from the land in the North to the land in the South.

'Soon,' said mothers to their children, 'soon now the Aqueduct will be finished. Then they will open the gates a thousand miles North and cool water will flow to us, for our crops, our flowers, our baths, and our tables.'

The children watched the Aqueduct being built stone on solid stone. It towered thirty feet in the sky, with great **gargoyle** spouts every hundred yards which would drop tiny streams down into yard reservoirs.

In the North there was not only one country, but two. They had rattled their sabres and clashed their shields for many years.

Now, in the Year of the Finishing of the Aqueduct, the two Northern countries shot a million arrows at each other and raised a million shields, like numerous suns, flashing. There was a cry like an ocean on a distant shore.

At the year's end the Aqueduct stood finished. The people of the Hot South, waiting, asked, 'When will the water come? With war in the North, will we starve for water, will our crops die?'

A courier came racing. 'The war is terrible,' he said. 'There is slaughtering that is unbelievable. More than one hundred million people have been slain.'

'For what?'

'They disagreed, those two Northern countries.

'That's all we know. They disagreed.'

---

gargoyle: in the shape of a human or animal mouth

The people gathered all along the stone Aqueduct. Messengers ran along the empty sluiceways with yellow streamers, crying, 'Bring vases and bowls, ready your fields and plows, open your baths, fetch water glasses!'

A thousand miles of filling Aqueduct and the slap of naked courier feet in the channel, running ahead. The people gathered by the tens of millions from the boiling countryside, the sluiceways open, waiting, their crocks, urns, jugs, held up toward the gargoyle spouts where the wind whistled emptily.

'It's coming!' The word passed from person to person down the one thousand miles.

And from a great distance, there was the sound of rushing and running, the sound that liquid makes in a stone channel. It flowed slowly at first and then faster, and then very fast down into the Southern land, under the hot Sun.

'It's here! Any second now. Listen!' said the people. They raised their glasses into the air.

Liquid poured from the sluiceways down the land, out of gargoyle mouths, into the stone baths, into glasses, into the fields. The fields were made rich for the harvest. People bathed. There was a singing you could hear from one field to one town to another.

'But, Mother!' A child held up his glass and shook it, the liquid whirled slowly. 'This isn't water!'

'Hush!' said the mother.

'It's red,' said the child. 'And it's thick.'

'Here's the soap, wash yourself, don't ask questions, shut up,' she said. 'Hurry into the field, open the sluicegates, plant the rice!'

In the fields, the father and his two sons laughed into one another's faces. 'If this keeps up, we've a great life ahead. A full **silo** and a clean body.'

'Don't worry,' said the two sons. 'The President is sending a representative North to make certain that the two countries there continue to disagree.'

'Who knows, it might be a fifty-year war!'

They sang and smiled.

And at night they all lay happily, listening to the good sound of the Aqueduct, full and rich, like a river, rushing through their land toward the morning.

---

silo: a store for grain

Activities

There Ain't Been No News by **Richard and Judy Dockrey Young**

1 **In pairs**, decide who will be **A** (a teenager) and who will be **B** (one of their parents, just back from work).

Make up a spoken story which begins with **A** saying:
'When I got home from school, I had an accident in the kitchen . . . But other than that, everything's been fine.'
B replies: 'The kitchen! What happened in the kitchen?'
A says: 'Well, that's easy to explain.' **[Gives a reason.]** 'But other than that, everything's been fine.'

Go on like this with **A** adding more and more details of disaster and **B** becoming more and more shocked.

Now swap roles. Invent another spoken story which begins with **B** (a teenager) telling **A** (a friend who has lent **B** their bike):
'When I was out on your bike yesterday, a tyre burst . . . But other than that, not a lot happened.'

Try to include five 'mounting disasters' in your stories. The last one should leave your partner speechless.

2 **a** **In small groups**, copy and complete the flow diagram below to show how *There Ain't Been No News* develops.

How *There Ain't Been No News* **develops**	
	Henry's dog died
which happened because . . .	↓
	it ate too much burned horse meat
which happened because . . .	↓ ▶

	Henry's barn burned down, killing the animals
which happened because . . .	↓
	?
which happened because . . .	↓
	?
	. . . and so on

b. **As a class** talk about:

- the **order** in which Fred chooses to tell Henry his items of news
- Fred's **repetition** of certain phrases.

Why does the humour of the story depend mainly on these two things?
Compare their effect with the spoken stories you made up in Activity 1.

3 **By yourself**, write a very short story with a similar structure to *There Ain't Been No News*. You could base it on one of these ideas:

- Oh, it's all been pretty boring, really
  A friend in your class has missed three weeks of school through illness. They want to know what everyone's been up to.

- We've had a very quiet time, dad/mum
  Your parents have been away for the weekend. They've left you and your brother/sister to look after the house. They are anxious to know how you coped.

- Not much has changed since you left
  A teenage friend has been on a space flight. They've been away for two months and are keen to find out what's been happening on Earth.

Ex Poser by **Paul Jennings** and *The One That Got Away* by **Jan Mark**

1 The narrator of *Ex Poser,* David, has different feelings as the story goes on. Often, he tries to keep them hidden from his classmates.

In small groups, chart David's *true* feelings by copying and filling in the *Truth Detector* below. Sometimes you will have to read 'between the lines', especially at the end of the story.

Truth Detector

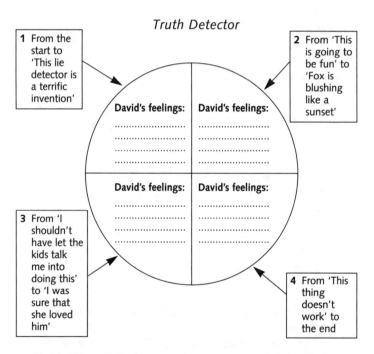

1 From the start to 'This lie detector is a terrific invention'

2 From 'This is going to be fun' to 'Fox is blushing like a sunset'

David's feelings:
....
....
....
....

David's feelings:
....
....
....
....

David's feelings:
....
....
....
....

David's feelings:
....
....
....
....

3 From 'I shouldn't have let the kids talk me into doing this' to 'I was sure that she loved him'

4 From 'This thing doesn't work' to the end

Finish this activity by agreeing on two sentences that say why the author chose to call his story *Ex Poser*. Write them underneath your Truth Detector.

Report back to the class.

2 *Ex Poser* is written in the **first person voice**. The narrator uses personal pronouns such as 'I', 'me', and 'my'.

In pairs, re-read paragraphs 3 and 4, from 'Sandra Morris is the same' to 'It's not fair'. Note down anything about the narrator's style which gives the impression he is talking aloud to the reader. Look at:

- his choice of language
- his choice of tense
- his way of constructing sentences
- his way of linking sentences.

Now re-write these paragraphs in the **third person voice** (using 'he', 'she') and the **past tense**. How does it change the effect? Do you think it improves the story or spoils it?

Report back to the class.

3 **By yourself**, write a story in which a person of your age tries to show up someone else but their plan backfires.

Use the first person voice and the present tense, as in *Ex Poser*.

4 **As a class**, re-read the last section of *The One That Got Away* from '"What's the matter?" Mrs Cooper said' to 'Chairs were overturned'.

a List all the **verbs** the author uses as alternatives to 'said'. What do they tell you about how the speakers are feeling?

b Now look at these sentences from earlier in the story:

- 'Something interesting, Mrs Cooper,' said everyone else, all together.
- 'It can't be a spider then,' said David, who was eavesdropping.
- 'It had an accident,' William said.

Suggest verbs which could take the place of 'said', telling you more about each speaker's tone of voice. Try thinking up **adverbs** to describe even more precisely the way David and William speak.

5 **In pairs**, compare the **plot** of *Ex Poser* with the plot of *The One That Got Away*. Copy and complete the comparison chart below to show what you decide.

Main features of the plot	*Ex Poser*	*The One That Got Away*
Setting	Secondary school	?
Central character	?	Malcolm
Basic situation	David uses Boffin's lie detector to try to show up Sandra and Ben Fox	?
The ending: how it depends on a 'twist'	?	?

Report back to the class.

Then **as a class** talk briefly about which of these school stories you enjoyed more. Explain your preference.

Feeding The Dog by **Susan Price** and *The Dancing Skeleton* by **Cynthia C. DeFelice**

1 **By yourself**, plan and write a shorter version of *Feeding The Dog* for 8–9 year olds.

You should:
- keep all the most important details of the plot
- make it as tense and frightening as possible
- use a style you think is suited to the age group
- include a coloured drawing of the 'thing'.

It would be ideal if you could show or read your version to an 8–9 year old, then report back their reaction to the class.

2 **As a class**, find five paragraphs in *Feeding The Dog* which use **adverbials of time** at or near their beginning, e.g. 'That night, Downing woke up.'

Draw on the board a vertical time-line. Mark off the story's main events according to the time when they happen. What patterns do you see?

Discuss why you think the author has taken such care to build up the story in a strict time sequence. Can you spot any other **structural devices** she has used?

3 **In pairs**, plan and draw a strip cartoon version of *The Dancing Skeleton*.

Base your first frame on paragraph 3 ('But that very night . . . '). Underneath, add the caption 'Aaron got up out of his grave, walked through the graveyard, and came home.'

You are likely to need about six frames in all. Each one must mark a new stage in the story. Give each one a suitable caption, quoted from the text.

You could put your finished work on display.

4 **As a class**, compare *Feeding The Dog* with *The Dancing Skeleton* in terms of **genre** and of **style**.

Base your discussion on these questions:

- One story has been published in a collection of *Horror Stories*. One has appeared in a collection of *Spooky Tales*. Which genre do you think each belongs to? Support your opinion by referring to the details of both texts, especially the author's choice of language.
- *The Dancing Skeleton* is a 'spoken story' whereas *Feeding The Dog* has a more conventional narrative style. On the board, list the main features of each style. Which is more successful in holding your attention?

No Exit by **Aoife Cahill** and *The Christmas Gift* by **Hugh Oliver**

1 *No Exit* is based on the **extended metaphor** of an unborn baby as a prisoner.

   In small groups, work out how the author makes comparisons, i.e. brings out similarities, between an unborn baby and a prisoner.

   Copy the diagrams below. Show your findings by writing quotations from the story into the spaces.

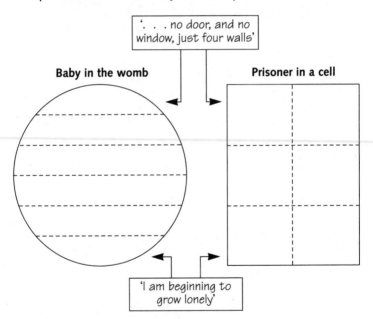

'. . . no door, and no window, just four walls'

Baby in the womb

Prisoner in a cell

'I am beginning to grow lonely'

   Allow yourself plenty of room to make at least six entries on your diagram.

   The author also draws contrasts, i.e. brings out differences, between a baby and a prisoner. Note these down separately in list form.

   Report back to the class.

2 As a class, look at the seven paragraphs of *No Exit* in turn. For each paragraph:
- agree on a brief heading which sums up its main topic
- choose one sentence, clause or phrase within the paragraph which you think captures its main topic well.

Now try re-arranging paragraphs 2 to 6. Would it matter if they came in a different order? How well do you think the whole story has been planned? Put forward your opinions by quoting details of the text.

3 By yourself, write a very short story based entirely on an extended metaphor. Plan carefully before you start. Do no more than three or four paragraphs.

Brainstorm ideas for your writing **as a class**. Other pupils have tried using the following comparisons:
- going to a disco and visiting another planet
- working your way through an exam paper and playing in a football match (or some other game)
- having a tooth taken out and being a building under demolition.

4 In small groups, look again at the eight sentences the stranger speaks in *The Christmas Gift*.

Discuss what they tell you about him. Show what you decide by making a note chart like this:

What the stranger says	What this shows about him
1 'Will you give me shelter?'	He has no home. He lives by relying on other people's kindness.
2 'I have much to do . . . And I have far to go.'	He travels far afield and keeps busy. It sounds as if he has a secret mission.
3 'In this world . . . I go wherever they will welcome me.'	?

Report back to the class.

Now **as a class**, talk about how the author has made the stranger into a *symbolic* character. What do you think he represents?

5 **As a class,** compare and contrast *No Exit* with *The Christmas Gift.*

Base your discussion on these questions:
- What similarities of **theme** are there in the stories? Are there important differences too?
- Why do you think the author of *No Exit* chose to write in the first person voice and the author of *The Christmas Gift* in the third person voice?
- How effective do you find the **endings** of the two stories? Which ending do you prefer, and why?

Spider's Web by **Kathleen Arnott** and *The Shrike and the Chipmunks* by **James Thurber**

1 These stories are **fables**. A fable is a story with animals as characters, not founded on fact, conveying a moral.

First look carefully at *The Shrike and the Chipmunks*. **In pairs**, work out in detail how the author's MORAL links back to what happens in this story.

Then agree on a suitable one-sentence moral for *Spider's Web*. Write it down, together with brief notes explaining why you chose it.

As a class, compare and justify your morals for *Spider's Web*. Vote for the best ones, and for the clearest explanations.

2 **In small groups**, compare the character of Hare in *Spider's Web* with the male chipmunk in *The Shrike and the Chipmunks*.

Do this by copying and completing the diagrams below:

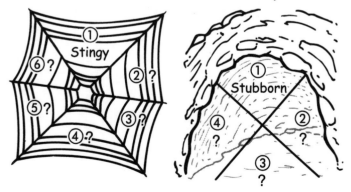

Hare

1. Stingy
6. ?
2. ?
5. ?
3. ?
4. ?

Male chipmunk

1. Stubborn
4. ?
2. ?
3. ?

For each point you make, find a quotation to back it up, for example:

> **Hare** ① Stingy: 'He chose his wife and made some excuse
> to her mother so that he did not pay the
> price immediately'
>
> **Male chipmunk** ① Stubborn: 'But he would not let her
> interfere with his designs'

When you have finished, **join up with another group**.
Compare ideas and quotations. Of the two characters,
which do you find the more appealing – and why?

3 **By yourself**, write a very short story in the form and style
of a *Fable for Today*.

EITHER: choose your own plot, characters and theme
OR: create your fable to illustrate one of these morals:
- Many Hands Make A Mess Of It
- Who Dares Loses
- A Friend In Need Is To Be Avoided
- Love Makes The World Go Mad
- Never Say Die – Just Keep Quiet.

Crossing by **Dennis Hamley**

1 **As a class**, use the evidence of the story to reconstruct George's motorbike ride *a year ago*. Map it out on the board. Use suitable symbols to illustrate each stage of George's journey: landmarks, distances, the scene of the accident, etc.

Then work **in pairs**. Take turns to describe to each other exactly what happened on 'that night a year ago'.

2 *Crossing* is a ghost story. **In small groups**, note down each reference you can find to show that George is not alone on his bike when he re-traces his steps a year after the accident. Do this by creating a ghost grid as follows:

Ghostly description	Its effect on George
1 'His tight-fitting riding leathers seemed to grip tighter round his waist as he leant into a right-hand bend'	This makes him feel that someone is riding pillion and clinging on to him for safety
2	

Make at least five entries on your grid.

At what point does George realize clearly whose ghost is riding with him? Why is it doing so?

Report back to the class.

3 **In pairs**:
   a Look carefully at the author's use of **verbs** to make his descriptions precise and vivid. Do this by copying the chart below and filling in the middle column with your opinions.

Verbs chosen	What effect do these verbs have?	Other possible choices
1 '. . . a cold nip in the rushing air <u>worried</u> at the visor of his helmet'	?	clutched tore
2 'As the Suzuki <u>urged</u> itself forward'	*Gives the impression the bike is very powerful and almost has a life of its own*	threw thrust
3 '<u>Roaring, bucketing</u> along, master of the smooth motor underneath him'	?	zooming rushing bouncing
4 '. . . if only the question that over-rode everything else would not keep <u>surging</u> into his mind'	?	rising floating
5 'But what he saw was <u>burned</u> in his mind . . .'	?	fixed imprinted

b Look again at these passages:

- 'Forty miles to go. In half an hour at that time of night? No trouble.'
- 'A mile. Half a mile. A car parked by the road just ahead. Pull out to pass it. Look in the mirror first.'

Each sentence is made deliberately **ungrammatical**. Say how. What effects do you think the author is aiming for by doing this?

Report back to the class on activities **a** and **b**.

4 **By yourself**, write a supernatural story woven around a journey. As you plan it out, think carefully about the effect you want your descriptions to have on the reader.

Digging for Trouble by **Marilyn Watts** and *Nightmare in Blue* by **Fredric Brown**

1 These stories contrast. The first is meant to be comic; the second is meant to be tragic.

In pairs, take one story each. Copy and complete the chart below to show how your story makes a comic OR tragic impression on the reader.

Features of comedy OR tragedy in: (name of story)		
The main events, including the climax	The feelings of the main characters as the story goes on	The author's style: descriptions, voice and tone

(If you are unsure what to write in column 3, ask your teacher for advice.)

When your charts are finished, put them together. Choose *one* contrasting point from *each column* which you agree brings out a strong difference between the stories.

Report your points back to the class.

2 **As a class**, look again at the *opening* of each story. In *Digging for Trouble*, re-read as far as 'I'm wasting time, aren't I? Sorry'. Re-read *Nightmare in Blue* as far as 'Get dressed then, and join me in the kitchen.'

Talk about the ways each author captures your interest and makes you want to read further. Include these questions in your discussion:
- How do the authors establish the **setting** of their story?
- What do you learn about the **character** of Sam in *Digging for Trouble* and George in *Nightmare in Blue*?

- What clues does each author give about what might happen later?
- What differences are there between **sentence length**, **voice** and **tone** in the two openings? Are these well suited to the kind of story each turns out to be?

3 a By yourself, write the opening of a story in *one* of these genres:

> • Crime   • Mystery   • Horror   • Fantasy
> • The Supernatural

Write about 150 words.

b Exchange openings **with a partner**. Write comments on your partner's work about how they have established:

- your interest in the events
- an impression of character(s) in the story
- the setting
- a writing style suited to the chosen genre.

c Now complete your own story. Take into account what you have learned from the comments about your story-telling skills.

Sting by **Paul Groves** and **Nigel Grimshaw** and *Breakfast* by **James Herbert**

1 **In small groups**, imagine you are a TV news team. You have been sent to Polven in Cornwall to report the invasion of the giant bees described in *Sting*.

Re-read the story from 'On the first of June the town of Polven had just breakfasted' to 'The watchers from the tanks saw the bees drop off the town hall one by one.'

Then, working together, compile a three-minute report for the ten o'clock news. Write it out as a script. Include:
- an introduction 'to camera' by a home affairs correspondent, outlining the main events of the day
- two film sequences (set them out in story-board form) with a 'voice over' for each
- interviews with several eye witnesses to events at different times during the invasion
- a summary and a hand-back to the TV studio.

Present your news report to the class and/or to a video camera.

2 **As a class**, use the board to fill in the evidence chart below. It requires you to look closely at the descriptive details in *Breakfast*.

Evidence that the woman's family have been dead for some time	Evidence that there has been a nuclear explosion

Then list *four* descriptions from different parts of the story which the author intends to *shock* you. Start with:

'A small creature with many eyelash legs stirred from its nest in the little girl's ear. It crawled out and scuttled into the dry white hair of the child's scalp.'

Look carefully at your completed list. Discuss the effect of:
- the author's use of similes and metaphors
- the word order of the sentences
- the placing of these descriptions next to others which are *not* meant to shock.

How effective to their purpose do you think these descriptions are?

3 Some stories set out mainly to entertain. Others set out to arouse strong feelings in the reader: for instance, to move us, to frighten us, to make us think about serious issues, etc.

In pairs, discuss which of these broad categories you would put *Sting* and *Breakfast* into. Think particularly about:
- the amount of *action* in each story
- how far each story makes you care about the *feelings* of those involved
- how *disturbing* you find each story, and why.

Report your ideas back to the class. Consider carefully any differences of opinion that emerge.

4 **By yourself**, write a horror story meant EITHER simply to entertain OR to make a serious point.

At the end, add a brief description of what you were trying to do in your story and the writing techniques you used to do it.

The Hand That Feeds Me by **Michael Z. Lewin** and *Dog, Cat, and Baby* by **Joe R. Lansdale**

1 'I was pleased with my justice' says the narrator at the end of *The Hand That Feeds Me*.

   a In small groups, work out how he makes sure the three murderers will be caught. Do it by creating a flow diagram like this:

Action	Purpose
1 Sniffs the scent of the murderers ➜	To pin them down to a particular part of the city
↓	
2 Finds and hides beer cans the murderers have handled ➜	?
↓	
?	?

   Report back to the class, referring to your finished diagrams.

   b As a class talk about the author's purposes in choosing a dog as his central character.
   What message do you think the story conveys?
   How is this emphasized by its title?

2 In *Dog, Cat, and Baby*, the viewpoint is that of two household pets.

   In pairs, discuss what the story shows about the feelings and thought processes of Dog and Cat. Compare them with those of the dog in *The Hand That Feeds Me*. Which portrayal of animals in these stories do you consider the more true-to-life?

   Report back to the class.

3 **As a class**, re-write in formal grammatical sentences the opening section of *Dog, Cat, and Baby*, down to 'Not way they loved Dog – before Baby'. Start like this:

> The dog did not like the baby. For that matter, the dog did not like the cat, but the cat had claws which were sharp . . .

Then talk about:
- how you have changed the author's style
- the most typical features of the author's chosen style
- *why* the story is written throughout in short phrases and sentences.

Now re-read the opening section of *The Hand That Feeds Me*, down to ' . . . but it was early so I moved on.' Compare the sentence structures with those of *Dog, Cat, and Baby*. Find examples of the author varying his sentences for effect.

Which author's style do you think is better suited to a story told from the viewpoint of animals?

4 **By yourself**, write EITHER a very short story OR a poem from an animal's point of view. Choose a form and style appropriate to your main character and the situation they are in.

Well, Well, Well by **Kate Hall**

1 **In pairs**, look at the following statements about what the author is saying in this story.

> **A** Abortion is wrong.
> **B** The mother is acting irresponsibly.
> **C** Teenagers have no right to interfere in their parents' lives.
> **D** Parents can be just as foolish as their children.
> **E** Everyone is entitled to live their lives as they wish.

Compare each of the statements with your own understanding of the story. Decide how far you agree/disagree with them.

Report back to the class. Does everyone hold the same view of the story's theme(s)?

2 The whole story is written as **direct speech** – that is, as a conversation.

As a class, re-write the first few lines into **reported speech**. Look carefully at what you have produced. Talk about:
- any changes you have made to the grammar (e.g. to **tense** and **voice**)
- any additional words you have introduced: what do they have in common?
- whether direct speech is more effective than reported speech for this story
- to which kinds of writing reported speech would be well suited.

3 **By yourself**, write a very short story made up entirely of direct speech. Limit it to two characters. They can be speaking face to face, on the telephone, or via e-mail.

As in *Well, Well, Well*, introduce some delayed information at the end which makes the reader review what they have read.

25

Reunion by **Arthur C. Clarke** and *Starbride* by **Anthony Boucher**

1 a In pairs, re-read *Reunion* aloud, alternating the paragraphs.

Working together, make notes for a *Revised History of Earth* based on what the speaker in the story says. Start like this:
- 10 million years ago, Earth was a tropical planet.
- It was adopted by the speaker's race as their home.
- They kept in contact with their home star via visiting starships.
- 2 million years ago . . .

When you have finished, report back to the class. Compare notes. Add or change any details you need to.

b By yourself, write up your *Revised History of Earth*. Write it in the style of a factual book aimed at young people aged 9–10. Think carefully about:
- your choice of language
- using a suitable voice and tone
- your paragraphing
- the length and structure of your sentences.

Use about 300 words. If possible, produce your piece on computer. Add suitable illustrations if you wish.

2 a In small groups, look back over *Starbride*. Work out:
- what happened to the Martian when he visited Earth
- what has since happened to Starbride
- why the narrator herself is planning to visit Earth.

Report back to the class.

b As a class, talk about how *Starbride* combines two story genres: Science Fiction and Romance. Use the board to list examples of the **plot**, the **characterization**, and the **style** typical of each genre to be found within this one story.

How successful do you consider the author's mixture of genres to be?

3 **By yourself**, write *one* of the following very short stories:

- 'We could have kept in touch, but there is so much to do in a universe of a hundred trillion stars.' (*Reunion*) Write a space adventure about the speaker's people set anywhere in the universe.

- Imagine that the narrator of *Starbride does* visit Earth. Describe her experiences. Write EITHER in the style of a Science Fiction story OR a Romance, or a mixture of both.

Sticks and Stones by **Annii Miethke** and *The Bridge* by **Jessie Kesson**

1 These stories describe young people who are excluded from their social group.

In small groups, discuss *why* Nola in *Sticks and Stones* and the youngest boy in *The Bridge* are treated as outsiders.

Then copy and complete the chart below to show *how* their group makes them feel rejected. Do it like this:

Nola	The youngest boy
1 Subjected to name-calling: 'Beachball . . . Fatty Fatty Boom Sticks . . . Piggy'	1 Put down for everything he does: 'I don't reckon it [the youngest boy's tiddler] much'
2 Has practical jokes played on her: 'Gym day changed, and their joke was not to tell Nola.'	2 Has to do dares which they think he'll fail: 'So you're not chicken . . . Prove it . . . Span the bridge and prove it.'

Make three more entries on your chart. Then, quoting evidence from the text, exchange opinions about which of these two outsiders suffers the most.

2 As a class:

a Re-read the opening section of *Sticks and Stones*, as far as 'They all developed and continued, increasing, cruelly cutting'.

In this section, the author's style is very compressed. She uses a 'snapshot' writing technique. Examine the way this works by looking at how she:
- switches viewpoints frequently
- signals the passing of time

- mixes dialogue and description
- uses different sentence structures, including one-word sentences.

b Scan the whole of *Sticks and Stones*. Trace the author's use of the 'beachball' metaphor throughout the story to describe Nola and her feelings. What part does this metaphor play in the final section?

3 **By yourself**, write a very short story about someone who is a victim of EITHER bullying OR peer-group pressure.

Use a 'snapshot' technique throughout, or in parts of, your story.

Teachers! by **Jane Morley** and *Soldier* by **Ben Rayner**

1 a In pairs, discuss the *main point* you think each author is making in their story. Write down one sentence that sums up the main point of *Teachers!* and one that does the same for *Soldier*.

Report back to the class.

b As a class consider how well the **form** and **style** of each story matches its author's intentions. Look in particular at:
- the change of time at the start of paragraphs in *Teachers!*
- the change of viewpoint at the start of the second paragraph in *Soldier*
- the mixing of description and dialogue in *Teachers!*
- the punchline effect of each story's ending.

2 In small groups, compose together a story of less than 100 words on *one* of the following topics:

> **A** Society's lack of care for nature and/or the countryside
> **B** Male-female relationships among teenagers
> **C** The double standards of some parents
> **D** Prejudice
> **E** The mixed blessings of computers.

When you have finished, exchange stories around the class. Drawing on your class discussion in Activity 1b, write brief comments on their effectiveness. Then compare opinions.

Vote for the stories which succeed best in matching form and style to content.

Court Martial by **Charles C. O'Connell** and *The Aqueduct* by **Ray Bradbury**

1 Both these stories are about war.

In small groups, draw up a comparison chart to show how each portrays war and fighting. Set it out like this:

Court Martial	The Aqueduct
1 A story about the insane violence and pointlessness of war: • the soldier is tortured and killed for an act of kindness • 'Men must one day realize the futility of bloodshed.'	**1** A story about the way some people always benefit in war from others' misfortunes: • the inhabitants of the South are able to survive only because of mass slaughter in the North • 'And at night they all lay happily, listening to the good sound of the Aqueduct . . .'

Make at least *three* further entries on your chart. Say whether you have found any differences, as well as similarities, in the view of war presented by the two authors.

Report back to the class.

2 **As a class** hold a debate on this topic:

War is never entirely good or entirely bad: some people's losses will always be other people's gains.

Use evidence from both stories, as well as using your own knowledge and research.

3 **As a class**, re-read the first and last paragraphs of *Court Martial*.
Consider:
- the different impression of the soldier's feelings given in each paragraph
- the way in which the language and sentence structure reflects this difference
- why the difference is important in conveying the story's theme.

Then look back over *The Aqueduct*. Find evidence that the author does not give **proper nouns** to the characters: instead, he uses **common nouns** and **pronouns**. Why do you think he does this? In your opinion, does it strengthen or weaken the story?

4 **By yourself**, choose a theme for creative writing about which you have strong feelings. Plan and draft a very short story of about 400 words on this theme.

Before writing your final version, glance back at the stories you have most enjoyed in this book. Then think carefully about:

- how to grab your reader's attention in the first paragraph
- the viewpoint (or viewpoints) you want to use in your story
- description, dialogue or a mixture of both?
- your choice of descriptive language – similes and metaphors, 'plain' language, or a mixture of both?
- suitable sentence lengths, and sentence structures, to reflect your theme
- your final paragraph, and your last sentence: with what feelings do you want to leave your reader?

Work on your story until you are completely satisfied that your reader will respond to the effects you have planned. Have it read and commented on both by your teacher and by other members of your class.

Chart relating Activities to NLS Objectives for KS3

An explanation of this chart is given in the 'Introduction for teachers' on page vii.

Title of Story	Main Framework Objectives covered in the Activities:				
	Sentence Level (S)	Text Level – Reading (R)	Text Level – Writing (W)	Speaking & Listening (S & L)	
There Ain't Been No News	7 S11	7 R7 7 R14	7 W2 7 W5	7 S&L2	
Ex Poser *The One That Got Away*	7 S4 7 S16	7 R8 7 R15	7 W6	7 S&L5	
Feeding The Dog *The Dancing Skeleton*	7 S8	7 R7 7 R12	7 W1 7 W10	7 S&L1 7 S&L13	
No Exit *The Christmas Gift*	7 S9 7 S12 7 S16	7 R2 7 R4 7 R8 7 R12	7 W6 7 W8	7 S&L1 7 S&L5	▲

Title of Story	Sentence Level (S)	Text Level – Reading (R)	Text Level – Writing (W)	Speaking & Listening (S & L)
Spider's Web *The Shrike and the Chipmunks*	7 S12	7 R6 7 R8 7 R9	7 W6 7 W7	7 S&L5 7 S&L7 7 S&L14
Crossing	8 S2 8 S4	8 R5 8 R7	8 W7	8 S&L2 8 S&L10
Digging for Trouble *Nightmare in Blue*	8 S2 8 S7	8 R5 8 R11	8 W1 8 W2	8 S&L11 8 S&L12
Sting *Breakfast*	8 S2	8 R8 8 R10	8 W5 8 W8	8 S&L2 8 S&L3 8 S&L15
The Hand That Feeds Me *Dog, Cat, and Baby*	8 S1 8 S3	8 R4 8 R5 8 R10	8 W6 8 W7	8 S&L10 8 S&L11
Well, Well, Well	9 S4 9 S9	9 R6 9 R12	9 W5	9 S&L5 9 S&L9

Title of Story	Sentence Level (S)	Text Level – Reading (R)	Text Level – Writing (W)	Speaking & Listening (S & L)
Reunion *Starbride*	9 S10	9 R6 9 R7	9 W1 9 W4	9 S&L2 9 S&L5
Sticks and Stones *The Bridge*	9 S2 9 S6	9 R6 9 R11	9 W5	9 S&L7 9 S&L10
Teachers! *Soldier*	9 S1	9 R3	9 W1 9 W2	9 S&L2
Court Martial *The Aqueduct*	9 S1 9 S4	9 R7 9 R9 9 R11	9 W1 9 W5	9 S&L2 9 S&L7

ALSO IN

Founding Editors: Anne and Ian Serraillier

Chinua Achebe Things Fall Apart
David Almond Skellig
Maya Angelou I Know Why the Caged Bird Sings
Margaret Atwood The Handmaid's Tale
Jane Austen Pride and Prejudice
Stan Barstow Joby; A Kind of Loving
Nina Bawden Carrie's War; Kept in the Dark; The Finding; Humbug
Malorie Blackman Tell Me No Lies; Words Last Forever
Ray Bradbury The Golden Apples of the Sun
Melvin Burgess and Lee Hall Billy Elliot
Betsy Byars The Midnight Fox; The Pinballs; The Eighteenth Emergency
Victor Canning The Runaways
Susan Cooper King of Shadows
Robert Cormier We All Fall Down; Heroes
Roald Dahl Danny, The Champion of the World; The Wonderful
Story of Henry Sugar; George's Marvellous Medicine; The Witches;
Boy; Going Solo; Matilda; My Year
Anita Desai The Village by the Sea
Charles Dickens A Christmas Carol; Great Expectations; A Charles
Dickens Selection
Berlie Doherty Granny was a Buffer Girl; Street Child
Roddy Doyle Paddy Clarke Ha Ha Ha
Anne Fine The Granny Project
Jamila Gavin The Wheel of Surya
Graham Greene Brighton Rock
Ann Halam Dr Franklin's Island
Thomas Hardy The Withered Arm and Other Wessex Tales
L P Hartley The Go-Between
Ernest Hemmingway The Old Man and the Sea; A Farewell to Arms
Barry Hines A Kestrel For A Knave
Nigel Hinton Getting Free; Buddy; Buddy's Song; Out of the Darkness
Anne Holm I Am David
Janni Howker Badger on the Barge; The Nature of the Beast;
Martin Farrell

Geraldine Kaye Comfort Herself
Daniel Keyes Flowers for Algernon
Dick King-Smith The Sheep-Pig
Elizabeth Laird Red Sky in the Morning; Kiss the Dust
D H Lawrence The Fox and The Virgin and the Gypsy; Selected Tales
Harper Lee To Kill a Mockingbird
C Day Lewis The Otterbury Incident
Joan Lingard Across the Barricades; The File on Fraulein Berg
Penelope Lively The Ghost of Thomas Kempe
Jack London The Call of the Wild; White Fang
Bernard MacLaverty Cal; The Best of Bernard Mac Laverty
Jan Mark Heathrow Nights
James Vance Marshall Walkabout
Ian McEwan The Daydreamer; A Child in Time
Michael Morpurgo My Friend Walter; The Wreck of the Zanzibar;
The War of Jenkins' Ear; Why the Whales Came; Arthur, High King
of Britain; Kensuke's Kingdom; From Hereabout Hill
Beverley Naidoo No Turning Back; The Other Side of Truth
Bill Naughton The Goalkeeper's Revenge
New Windmill Book of Challenging Texts: Thoughtlines
New Windmill A Charles Dickens Selection
New Windmill Book of Classic Short Stories
New Windmill Book of Fiction and Non-fiction: Taking Off!
New Windmill Book of Humorous Stories: Don't Make Me Laugh
New Windmill Book of Nineteenth Century Short Stories
New Windmill Book of Non-fiction: Get Real!
New Windmill Book of Non-fiction: Real Lives, Real Times
New Windmill Book of Scottish Short Stories
New Windmill Book of Short Stories: A Winter's Cauldron
New Windmill Book of Short Stories: Fast and Curious
New Windmill Book of Short Stories: From Beginning to End
New Windmill Book of Short Stories: Into the Unknown
New Windmill Book of Short Stories: Tales with a Twist
New Windmill Book of Short Stories: Trouble in Two Centuries
New Windmill Book of Short Stories: Ways With Words
New Windmill Book of Stories from Many Cultures and Traditions:
Fifty-Fifty Tuti-Fruity Chocolate Chip
New Windmill Book of Stories from Many Genres: Myths, Murders
and Mysteries

How many have you read?